R YEAR

Classworks

Numeracy

Helen Williams

Published in 2003 by:
Nelson Thornes Ltd
Delta Place
27 Bath Road
CHELTENHAM
GL53 7TH
United Kingdom

03 04 05 06 07 / 10 9 8 7 6 5 4 3 2 1

A catalogue record for this book is available from the British Library

ISBN 0 7487 7334 7

Illustrations by Tim Oliver and Cathy Hughes
Page make-up by Hart McLeod
Cover photograph © Corbis EI 170 (NT)
Printed in Great Britain by Ashford Colour Press

CLASSWORKS – BLUEPRINTS – LEARNING TARGETS – LASTMINUTELESSON.CO.UK

Nelson Thornes publishes teacher's resource books packed with flexible ideas for use in primary schools. As well as *Classworks*,
Nelson Thornes publishes *Blueprints* and *Learning Targets*, providing busy teachers with unbeatable curriculum coverage, inspiration
and value for money. We mail teachers and schools about new Nelson Thornes publications regularly. To join the mailing list simply
photocopy and complete the form below and return using the FREEPOST address to receive regular updates on our new and existing
titles. Books can be bought by credit card over the telephone or internet. For more details log on to www.nelsonthornes.com or contact
us on 01242 267 280.
For FREE resources register at www.lastminutelesson.co.uk

Please add my name to the Nelson Thornes Teacher's Resources mailing list.

Mr/Mrs/Miss/Ms _____

Address _____

_____

_____

Postcode _____

School address _____

_____

_____

Postcode _____

To: Direct Marketing Coordinator, Nelson Thornes Ltd, FREEPOST SWC 0507,
Cheltenham GL53 7ZZ

Contents

Contents

CONTENTS

Introduction

Young children have a natural curiosity about what is around them, and this includes the mathematical. A critical factor in young children's mathematical development is to provide appropriate opportunities for them to play. Classworks *suggests a range of rich and playful contexts to promote Reception children's mathematical development.*

How *Classworks* Works

Practical ideas

- *Classworks* prioritises practical work. The Reception year is a unique year. No Reception class is the same as any other. Children arrive in this, their final year of the Foundation Stage, at different times and with many differing experiences. *Classworks* recognises this richness by providing mathematically rich but simple ideas, using a wide range of resources, that can be developed in several ways to suit the maturity and experience of the children.

Play

- The most effective early learning takes place when there is a balance between child-initiated and adult-led activities. *Classworks* combines suggestions for focused group activities with suggestions for encouraging free mathematical exploration. Children need opportunities to play independently, making their own mathematical decisions and developing their own ideas.

- In addition, each activity includes suggestions for adult questions that encourage the children to solve the problem themselves, for example: 'How can you?' 'What will you try next?'

Repetition

- In order for the mathematics to come to the forefront, with children recognising patterns, similarities and differences, activities need to be simple, enjoyable and easily repeated. This helps children gain a sense of control over the mathematics involved. Repeating the same task with different resources helps establish links between various activities, and encourages children to apply knowledge learned in one situation to another. *Classworks* activities are designed to be repeated, with options of differing levels of difficulty over the course of the Reception year.

Communication

- Children learn by talking to each other and to adults about what they are doing and what they notice – talk is the link between doing something and knowing something. *Classworks* prioritises communication between children by making many of the activities for pairs of children working alongside each other, and later collaboratively.

Modelling

- It is important that children have opportunities to observe both each other and adults engaged in mathematics. *Classworks* activities are built around tasks that are modelled and discussed.

What each page does

Clear, simple description of the activity

Area of maths and mathematical background clearly set out

Early learning goals and stepping stones signalled

Who should do the activity, and what they need to be able to do already

Key vocabulary to look for

Clear description of the key activities, with questions to ask and artwork where appropriate

How you can change the activity to make it easier or more challenging

Learning outcome in child-friendly language

Resources necessary for the activity

Points to look out for in plenary sessions

Things to do leading from this activity

Complementary activities covering similar or related areas of maths

Explanatory artwork where appropriate

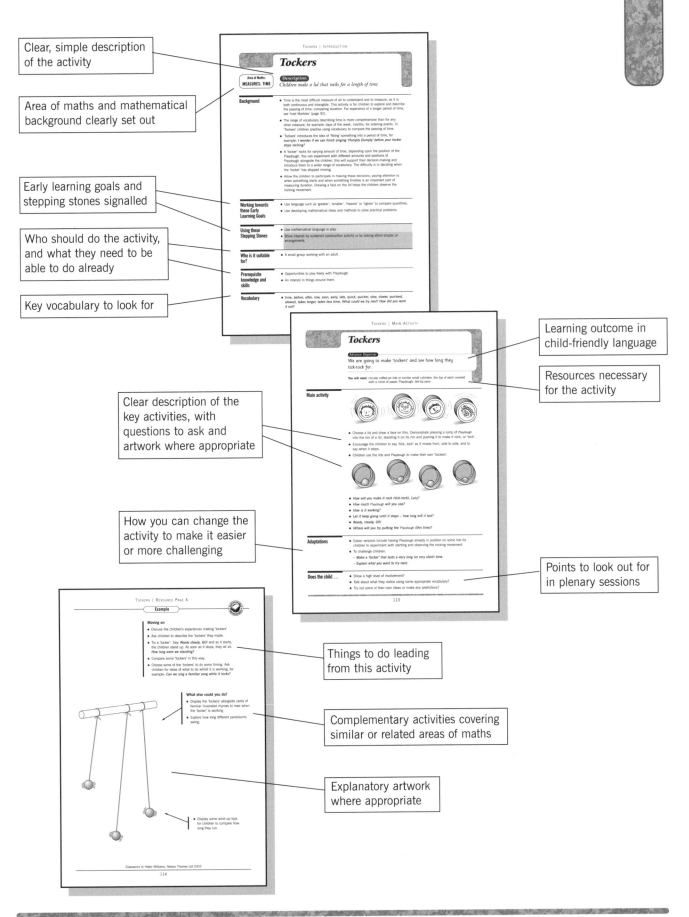

Use Them All

Area of Maths:
MAINLY NUMBER

Description

Children use interlocking cubes to make models, each with five cubes. These are used to compare similarities and differences.

Background

- Recognising similarities and differences is fundamental to mathematics. Here, keeping each child's cubes to a single colour helps them focus on the shapes rather than the array of colours in any one model. It will still take time for some children to see this yellow shape as similar to this blue shape – as they are obviously different colours.

- Focus on them saying what they see as the same, for example, 'This one has an arm sticking out like this one', rather than an overall difference or similarity.

- The 'mat' (resource page A) helps them keep the number of cubes constant each time, although expect some children to add cubes to make their model more attractive! It is difficult to count the fixed cubes in a model, and they may well count the same cubes more than once. Ask if they know how many there are without counting again.

Working towards these Early Learning Goals

- Count reliably up to ten every-day objects.

- Say and use number names in familiar contexts.

- In practical activities and discussion, begin to use the vocabulary involved in adding and subtracting.

- Use developing mathematical ideas and methods to solve practical problems.

Using these Stepping Stones

- Use mathematical language in play.

- Show an interest in numbers and counting.

- Use some number names and number language spontaneously.

- Willingly attempt to count, with some numbers, in the correct order.

- Show curiosity about numbers by offering comments or asking questions.

- Recognise groups with one, two or three objects.

- Count up to three or four objects by saying one number name for each item.

- Count an irregular arrangement of up to ten objects.

Who is it suitable for?

- A small group as an independent activity.

Prerequisite knowledge and skills

- Free play with interlocking cubes.

- An ability to invent something to make.

- Experience of counting small numbers of objects.

Vocabulary

- *one, two, three, four, five, count, more, less, fewer, larger, greater, one more, one less*

Use Them All

We are going to make models from five cubes

You will need: resource pages A–C, trays of interlocking cubes each in a single colour

Main activity

- Give each child a 'Use Them All' mat as on resource page A, and a tray of cubes in a single colour.
- 'Read' the numeral together, trace over it with a finger.
- They count five cubes onto the mat, using the squares to help.
- They then clip all five together to make a model.
- They make different models each with five cubes, keeping the models they make.
- *What does this one look like?*
- *How do you know you have exactly five cubes in your model?*
- *What have you chosen to make?*
- *How is this one like (different from) this one?*
- *Can you make a different model with five cubes?*

Adaptations

- An easier version is to use resource page B to make models with four cubes.
- Further challenges include:
  - *Can you draw any of your models?*
  - *Bet you can't make some different 5-models!*

Does the child ...

- Accurately count five objects from a larger collection?
- Keep the number of cubes in each model constant?
- Make some different shapes all with the same number of cubes?
- Comment on the shapes and the numbers of cubes?

Pupil page

Use Them All

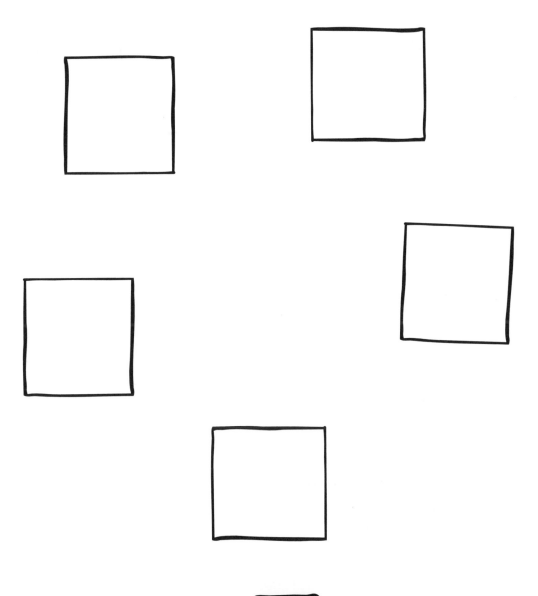

(Pupil page)

Use Them All

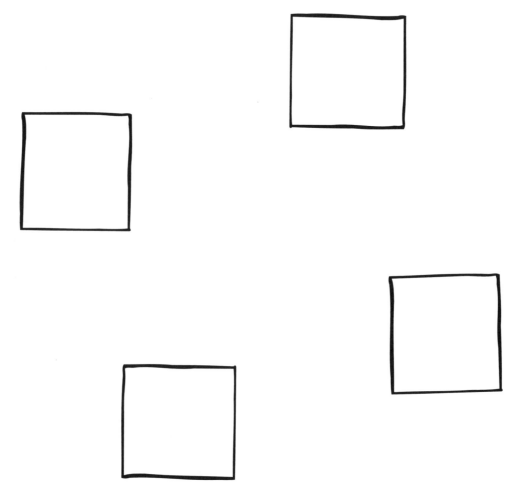

Pupil page

Use Them All

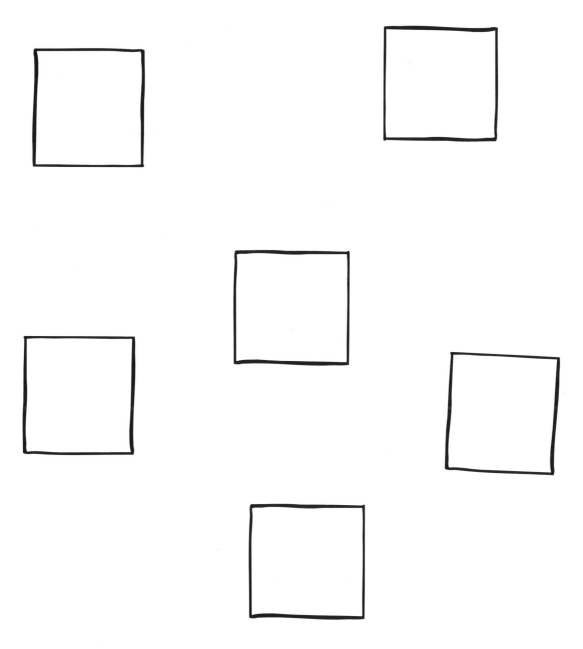

Developments

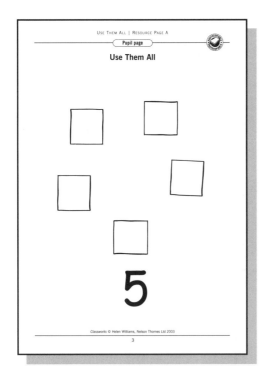

Moving on

- Display all the 5-cube shapes for the children to handle and discuss. Invite them to choose a shape to talk about. Can they find another model the same as, or different from, the one they are holding?

- Children can work in pairs, discussing and choosing a model they like, to make one just the same.

What else could you do?

- Use mixed colours of cubes: can they recognise similar shapes?

- Try a different number for the 'Use them all' mat.

- Use different construction apparatus, such as Lego, to make 5-models.

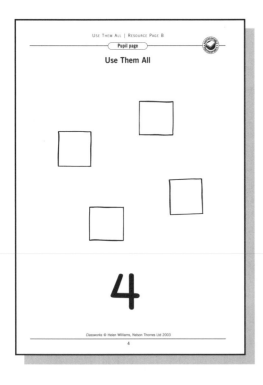

Under the Box

Area of Maths:
MAINLY NUMBER AND CALCULATING

Description

Five toys are hidden under a box, and some taken out for children to calculate the 'hidden number'.

Background	<ul><li>This is an example of 'partitioning' an amount into its complements (or number pairs) (see also 'Eating worms' page 64 and 'Gold Up 2' page 58). 'Under the Box' extends partitioning further, by hiding one of these pairs so that the children must calculate the 'missing number'.</li><li>The total must be kept constant each time the game is played.</li><li>To be effective, this game is played regularly, with a range of apparatus. Remember to point out similarities so they don't just think each is a new experience!</li><li>Gradually, you can extend this activity to working with the complements of numbers up to ten.</li></ul>
Working towards these Early Learning Goals	<ul><li>Count reliably up to ten every-day objects.</li><li>Say and use number names in familiar contexts.</li><li>Use developing mathematical ideas and methods to solve practical problems.</li><li>Use language such as 'more' or 'less' to compare two numbers.</li><li>In practical activities and discussion, begin to use the vocabulary involved in adding and subtracting.</li><li>Begin to relate addition to combining two groups of objects and subtracting to 'taking away'.</li></ul>
Using these Stepping Stones	<ul><li>Comparing two groups of objects, saying when they have the same number.</li><li>Show an interest in numbers and counting.</li><li>Use some number names and number language spontaneously.</li><li>Separate a group of three or four objects in different ways, beginning to recognise that the total is still the same.</li><li>Show curiosity about numbers by offering comments or asking questions.</li><li>Sometimes show confidence and offer solutions to problems.</li></ul>
Who is it suitable for?	<ul><li>Large or small group with adult; later as an independent activity.</li></ul>
Prerequisite knowledge and skills	<ul><li>Familiarity with 'Gold Up 2' (page 58), or similar partitioning activity.</li><li>Confidence in counting and recognising groups of up to 5 items.</li></ul>
Vocabulary	<ul><li>*one, two, three …, How many … ?, How many are left?, How many have gone?*</li></ul>

Under the Box

We are going to work out how many toys are hidden under the box

You will need: five soft toys, a box large enough to hide these

Main activity

- Look at and count the toys together.
- Cover them all with a large, upturned box.
- Take some from under the box and put them on top .
- Ask the children to work out how many are still hidden under the box.
- Children can repeat the game with a partner, hiding a set of five play-people in a small box. Encourage them to talk about the numbers each time.
- *How many toys did we start with?*
- *How many have I taken out of the box?*
- *How many are left under the box?*
- *How do you know?*
- *Are you sure?*
- *How did you work that out?*

Adaptations

- An easier version is to use four identical toys.
- Further challenges include:
  - Use a larger number of toys.
  - *Let's pretend I have taken out 3 toys. How many are left under the box?*

Does the child ...

- Attempt to work out how many are missing?
- Remember the total number of toys?
- Explain their ideas?

(**Developments**)

Moving on

- Talk with the children about their experiences of playing 'Under the Box'.

- Invite the children to model and explain something that happened when they played, using the props.

- Play again, but this time remove the toys secretly and then lift the box. Children have to work out the number of toys removed by counting those remaining.

What else could you do?

- Tell a story to match each 'turn': *There are five toys in the bed, one doll gets up ... How many are left in bed?*

- Change the resources you play with: for example, play it 'big' hiding 5 children in a large box.

- Play it 'small' with treasure items hidden in a treasure bag.

Tray of Sweets

Area of Maths:
MAINLY NUMBER

Description

Children fill boxes with compartments, counting and comparing how many each holds.

Background

- Using containers with compartments keeps this task to a manageable number to count and compare.
- Give each child the time and opportunity to fill different sizes of tray. After they have filled a few, discuss and compare the number each tray holds.

Working towards these Early Learning Goals

- Count reliably up to ten every-day objects.
- Say and use number names in familiar contexts.
- Use developing mathematical ideas and methods to solve practical problems.
- Recognise numerals 1 to 9.
- Use language such as 'more' or 'less' to compare two numbers.

Using these Stepping Stones

- Show an interest in numbers and counting.
- Use some number names and number language spontaneously.
- Willingly attempt to count, with some numbers in the correct order.
- Show curiosity about numbers by offering comments or asking questions.
- Recognise numerals 1 to 5, then 1 to 9.
- Select the correct numeral to represent one to five, then one to nine, to describe objects.

Who is it suitable for?

- A small group working independently.

Prerequisite knowledge and skills

- Counting experiences to ten.
- Opportunities to read numerals.
- Free play with Playdough.

Vocabulary

- *one, two, three ..., How many ...?, count, more, less, fewer, largest*

Tray of Sweets

We are going to make trays of sweets and count them

You will need: lots of different sizes of tray from chocolate boxes, Playdough, wooden or similar numerals to match the full trays (optional), clean sweet wrappers, resource pages A to C to line trays, if necessary

Main activity

- Give each child an empty chocolate tray.
- Ask them to make enough Playdough 'sweets' to fill their tray, one in each compartment.
- They count how many their tray holds altogether and find the correct numeral for their full tray.

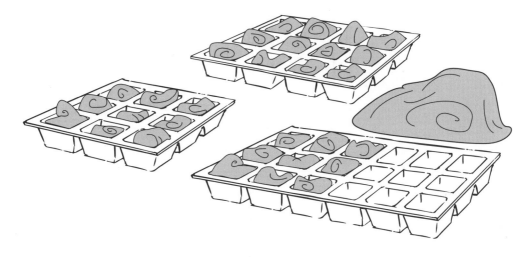

- *How many have you made so far?*
- *How many are left to make?*
- *How many sweets do you think this tray will hold?*
- *Which tray holds the most (fewest) sweets?*

Adaptations

- An easier activity is using ready-made 'sweets', such as beads.
- Further challenges include:
  - Find two trays that hold the same number of items.
  - *Put two small sweets in each compartment. Now how many does your tray hold?*

Does the child ...

- Place one object in each compartment systematically?
- Count the total number of items and find the correct number card?
- Compare the number of items in different trays?

Tray of Sweets

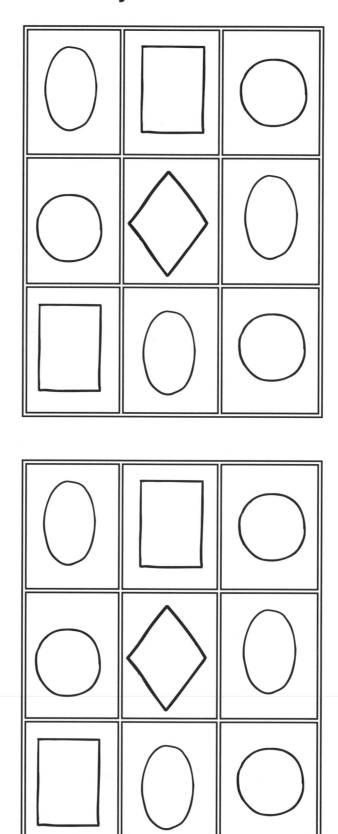

Tray of Sweets

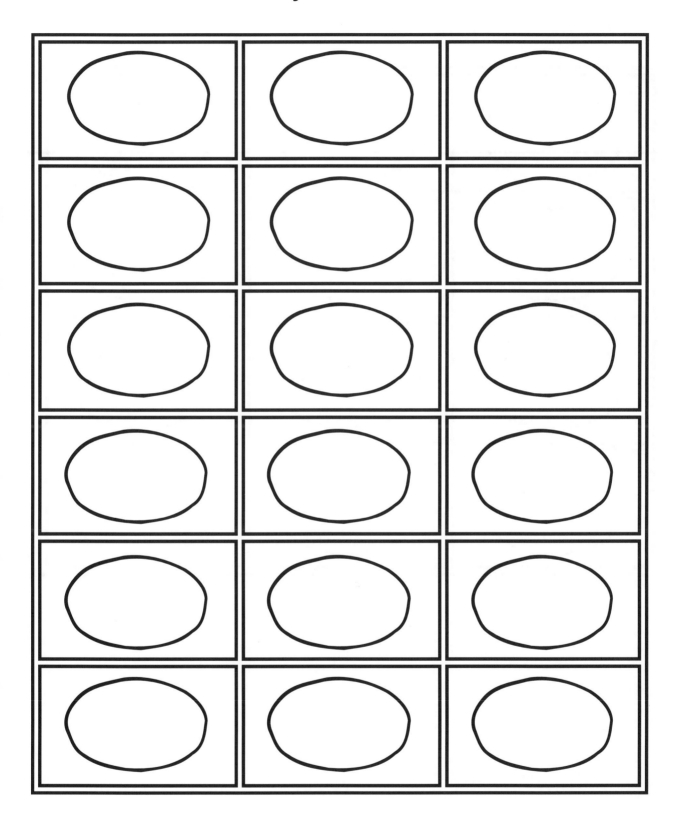

Tray of Sweets

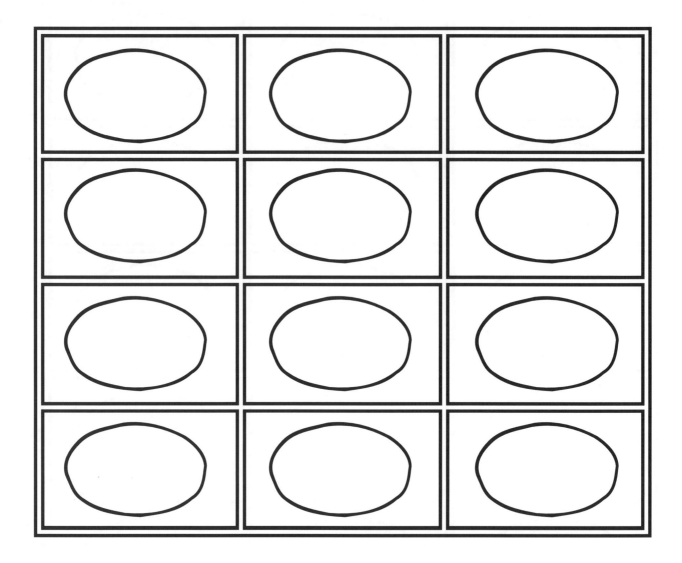

Tray of Sweets

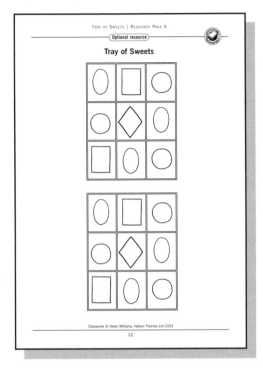

Moving on

- Use Playdough in three or four colours. Children decide how many sweets of each colour to include in their trays.

- They count and find a way of recording the numbers of sweets in different colours in the trays.

What else could you do?

- Make Playdough buns for bun tins, or eggs for egg boxes.

- Make real buns in bun tins.

- Put different items in the compartments, such as buttons, shells, beads, and so on.

Steven's Shopping

Area of Maths:
MAINLY NUMBER AND CALCULATING

Description

The picture book 'The Shopping Basket' by John Burningham (Red Fox, 2000) is used to illustrate the vocabulary associated with addition and subtraction.

Background

- The triangular pattern of counting numbers is a powerful illustration of 'one more' and 'one less / fewer'. Provide a display of this pattern, using a variety of apparatus in various orientations for the children to explore and you to discuss with them.

- Making 'staircases' with a range of apparatus will support this idea.

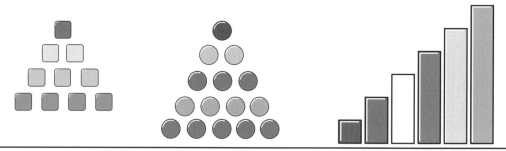

Working towards these Early Learning Goals

- Count reliably up to ten every-day objects.

- Say and use number names in familiar contexts.

- Use developing mathematical ideas and methods to solve practical problems.

- Use language such as 'more' or 'less' to compare two numbers.

- In practical activities and discussion, begin to use the vocabulary involved in adding and subtracting.

- Find one more or one less than a number from one to ten.

- Begin to relate addition to combining two groups of objects and subtracting to 'taking away'.

Using these Stepping Stones

- Show an interest in numbers and counting.

- Use some number names and number language spontaneously.

- Willingly attempt to count, with some numbers in the correct order.

- Show curiosity about numbers by offering comments or asking questions.

- Begin to represent numbers using fingers, marks on paper, or pictures.

- Say with confidence the number that is one more than a given number.

Who is it suitable for?

- Large or small group with an adult.

Prerequisite knowledge and skills

- Familiarity with the story.

- Counting experiences to six.

Vocabulary

- *more, fewer, less, one more, one less/fewer, compare, one, two, three ...*

Steven's Shopping

We are going to count Steven's shopping

You will need: picture book, 'The Shopping Basket' by John Burningham for each pair of children: a shopping bag containing shopping items from the book; six eggs, five bananas, four apples, three oranges, two doughnuts and one packet of crisps (mini-fruit or vegetables can be used), resource page A (per child)

Main activity

- After reading the story together, ask the children to look at the bag of shopping items, sorting them and laying them out in order, as shown in the book.

- Encourage them to work in pairs to retell the story, removing the items as they are stolen by the characters.

- *What did he buy most of?*

- *Can you lay them out in order from the most to the least?*

- *How many (...) did his mother ask for?*

- *Can you count the eggs to make sure we have 6?*

- *Are you sure we have the right number of (...)?*

- *Do we have all the things Steven was sent to buy?*

- *Can you see/talk about the pattern of the numbers?*

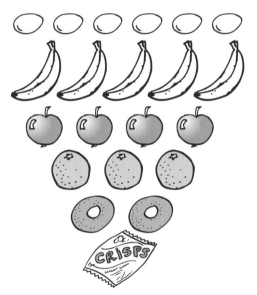

Adaptations

- An easier version is to model laying out and counting the eggs and the bananas. Then lay out and count the remaining items. Reread the book, counting the real items each time. Give the children a mat on which to lay out the items such as those on resource page B.

- Further challenges include:

  - Arrange the items from memory and match numeral cards one to six to each row.

  - Record the items of shopping on paper.

  - Make Cuisenaire rod staircases using resource page A.

Does the child ...

- Count the real items accurately?

- Use words like 'one more' and 'one less' when asked about the 6, 5, 4, 3, 2, 1 arrangement?

- Demonstrate some independence and confidence when tackling the task?

Steven's Shopping
Make staircases

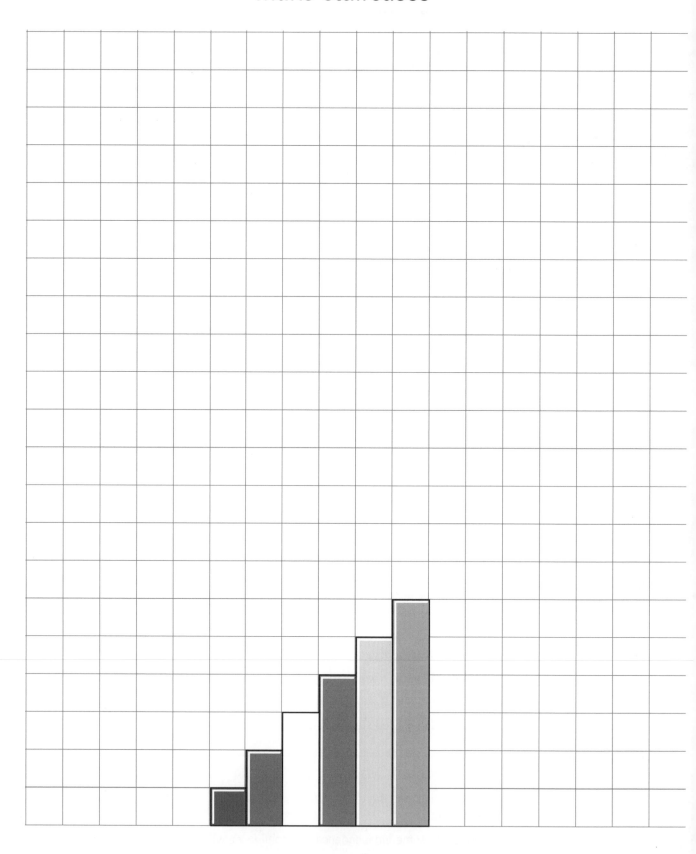

Developments

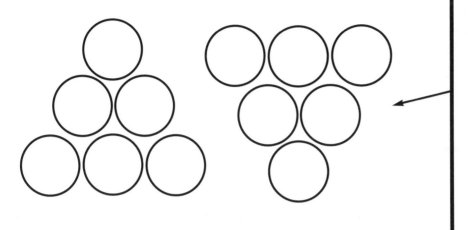

Moving on

- The six, five, four, three, two, one arrangement can be reproduced with different apparatus: *Who can use these transparent counters to make the number pattern that Steven's shopping made?*

- Use the characters in the story to play a disappearing game: the children hide their eyes while you remove or re-position items of shopping. When they open their eyes, can they tell you what has changed and how they know?

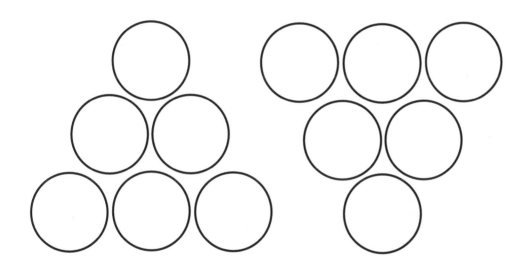

What else could you do?

- Children retell the story to each other using the props.

- Invite the children to invent a new shopping story using the props.

- Extend the story up to ten items: *What else could Steven's mum send him to buy?*

- Try building a triangle pattern of the counting numbers from one at the top: *How far can we go?*

Roland Robot

Area of Maths:
MAINLY NUMBER

Description

Roland Robot encourages children to visualise and to work from their visual image to construct a cube-model. Models are then compared in terms of similarities and differences of shape and amounts.

Background

- As mathematics is a mental activity, visualisation is an important skill to develop at all levels.

- Offering 'peeps' moves children from working directly by laying cubes on the picture, into being supported whilst working in their heads. Offer as many peeps as you, or they, like.

- Using cubes in one colour helps children focus on the shape and the numbers when comparing the resulting models.

Working towards these Early Learning Goals

- Count reliably up to ten every-day objects.
- Say and use number names in familiar contexts.
- Use developing mathematical ideas and methods to solve practical problems.
- Use language such as 'more' or 'less' to compare two numbers.
- Use everyday words to describe position.

Using these Stepping Stones

- Show an interest in numbers and counting.
- Use some number names and number language spontaneously.
- Show curiosity about numbers by offering comments or asking questions.
- Count an irregular arrangement of up to ten objects.
- Sometimes show confidence and offer solutions to problems.

Who is it suitable for?

- Group working independently. Size of group depends upon number of cubes available in a single colour.

Prerequisite knowledge and skills

- Familiarity with the cubes.
- A willingness to make a model clipping the cubes together and to name it, for example: 'I made a dog – look here are its legs'.

Vocabulary

- *one, two, three ..., more, less, fewer, imagine, remember, use, make, build*

Roland Robot

We are going to make Roland Robot using cubes

You will need: linking cubes in a single colour, resource page A copied onto an overhead transparency (OHT) to use with an overhead projector (OHP), if available

Main activity

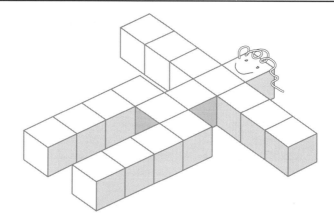

- Use resource page A to show the group some quick 'peeps' of Roland Robot.

- Encourage them to talk about how he is made after each peep. Provide cubes of one colour for them to make their Roland Robots.

- When all the robots have been made, compare them with each other and with the picture.

- *That was just a peep. Would you like another peep?*

- *What did you see that time?*

- *Try to picture Roland Robot in your head.*

- *How many cubes will you use for his legs (arms...)?*

- *Are all your Roland Robots the same?*

- *How are they different?*

- *Amy's Roland has longer legs. Why is that?*

Adaptations

- An easier version is to give children a large tray of cubes in a single colour and ask them to make a robot of their own design with arms and legs.

- Further challenges include:

  – Asking children to record their robot accurately on squared paper.

  – *How many cubes does it take to make Roland?*

  – *Can you make Roland's big sister, Reema? (She uses 25 cubes.)*

Does the child ...

- Make a robot similar to, or the same as, Roland?

- Make observations about differences and/or similarities between the models?

- Use counting when making or comparing the models?

Roland Robot

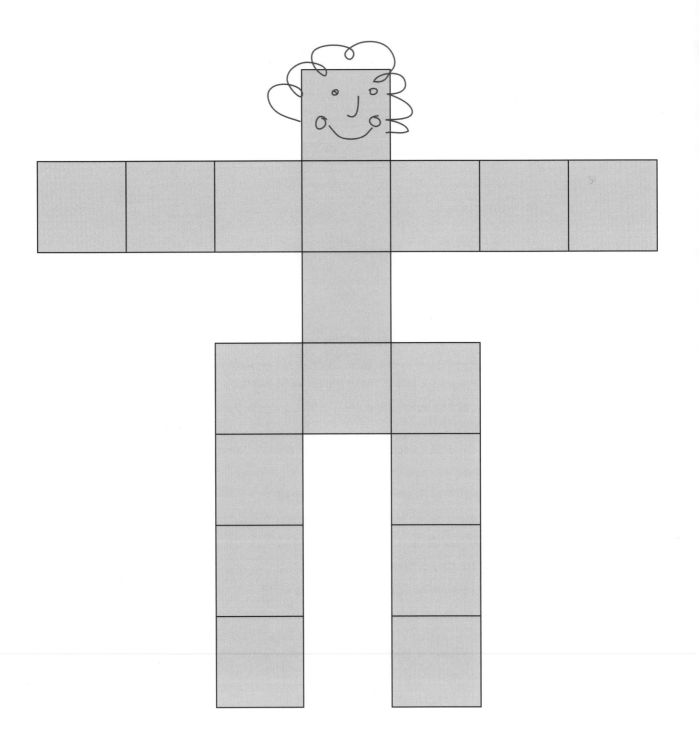

Developments

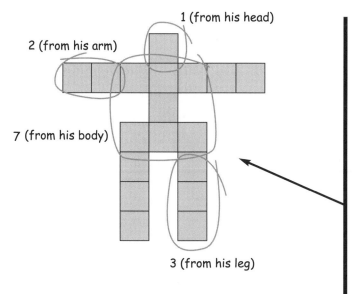

1 (from his head)

2 (from his arm)

7 (from his body)

3 (from his leg)

Moving on

- Remind the children that they worked in their **heads** to make their robots. Discuss how they did this; *'We closed our eyes'*, *'We had a lot of peeps'*, and so on.

- Discuss the completed robots in terms of the number of cubes used; *'How long are his arms?'*, *'How many cubes make up his body?'*, *'Which cube shall we count from/to?'*...

- You may want to model how to record the number of cubes used for each body part.

- Give the children a different colour of cube. Ask them to make a robot family and to remember to count when they make each one. Provide pencil and paper for them to remember what they have counted.

- When the models are completed, encourage the children to talk about what they have made as well as how they tackled the task. Remind them to tell you about how and when they counted.

- If the children have done any recording, display this for discussion.

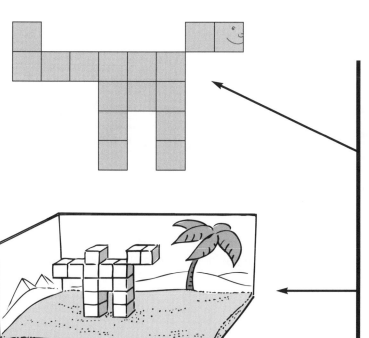

What else could you do?

- Children select number cards and make towers for each card. They join their towers together to make a robot.

- Use these same towers to make an animal.

- Create a cube animal such as a dog or camel. Name it. As with Roland Robot, use this as a 'template' to make the same animal in different colours.

- Display the models in an 'environment' such as a desert, using sand and a backdrop to stimulate new model-making ideas.

Pass It On

Area of Maths:
MAINLY NUMBER

Description

'Pass It On' provides opportunities to practise counting small numbers of selected objects in a game context. There are no 'winners' or 'losers', simply active participants.

Background

- Playing 'Pass It On' many times will help children become confident with how the game works (who rolls when, and so on). Gradually they will begin to observe and predict, for example, 'If I get a two, I'll have none left!'

- Playing the game with different resources helps the children use developing skills and knowledge in many different contexts.

- For children to play independently, the adult must step back from organising the turn-taking.

Working towards these Early Learning Goals

- Count reliably up to ten every-day objects.

- Say and use number names in familiar contexts.

- Use language such as 'more' or 'less' to compare two numbers.

- In practical activities and discussion, begin to use the vocabulary involved in adding and subtracting.

- Use developing mathematical ideas and methods to solve practical problems.

Using these Stepping Stones

- Show an interest in numbers and counting.

- Use some number names and number language spontaneously.

- Willingly attempt to count, with some numbers in the correct order.

- Show curiosity about numbers by offering comments or asking questions.

- Count out up to six objects from a larger group.

Who is it suitable for?

- A group of four sitting around a table working independently.

Prerequisite knowledge and skills

- Opportunities to handle and discuss the tray of interesting objects or 'treasure'.

- Experience of taking a turn in a game.

- Knowledge of the role of dice in games.

- Ability to count to three.

Vocabulary

- *one, two, three ..., How many ...?, count, more, fewer, add, and, make, sum, total, altogether*

Pass It On

We are going to roll the dice and pass that many buttons on

You will need: a mixture of small interesting objects such as shells, cracker toys, buttons, and coins, a paper plate for each player, a one-to-three dot die for each player or resource page A to cover ordinary dice

Main activity

- *Come and play 'Pass It On'.*

- Give each child a plate and let them select some 'treasure' to put on their plate. They talk about their chosen items. When they are happy with their selection, ask if they would like to play a game using their treasure.

- Each child has their own die but they take it in turns to roll. When they roll a 'three dots' they choose three items from their plate to pass on to the person next to them.

- Play continues around the table, each child rolling a die and choosing that number of items from their collection to pass on.

- *Why have you chosen that button?*

- *What will you choose to pass to Zoe?*

- *How many do you have to pass on?*

- *What do you do now?*

- *What happens next?*

- *Whose turn is it?*

Adaptations

- An easier version is to omit the dice. In turn, each child chooses one (or two) items to pass on to the next player.

- Further challenges include:

  – You pass on one, two or three things that are similar (two buttons, two coins, and so on).

  – *What happens if we use a die which includes a zero?* Adapt a cover from resource page A.

Does the child ...

- Willingly talk about his/her selected items?

- Count the items accurately to match the die-roll?

- Respond to, or initiate, discussions about what is happening; for example, 'Look – I've got no feathers left!'

Pupil page

Pass It On

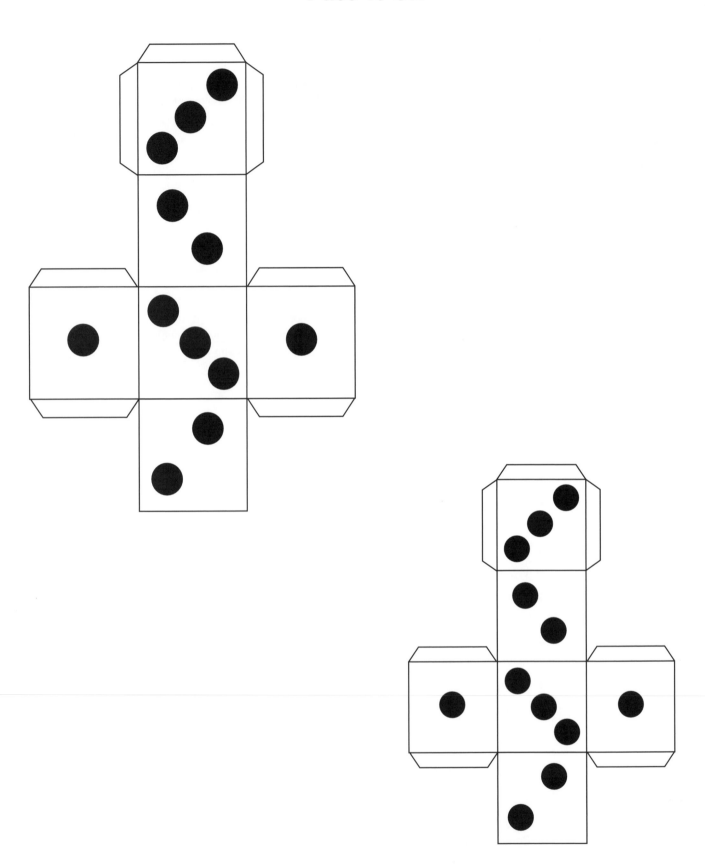

Developments

Moving on

- Ask the children to recall how the game was played.

- Encourage them to remember and tell us something that happened, for example, you rolled three but only had two items left on your plate. What did you do?

- Talk about how they chose something to pass on.

- Ask for volunteers to play the game today. If possible, an experienced player can teach a novice.

- Let them make decisions about the items to play with and how to organise the game.

- You may consider 'fixing' the number of items they begin with, in order that someone runs out at some point. Ask for solutions about how to solve this problem.

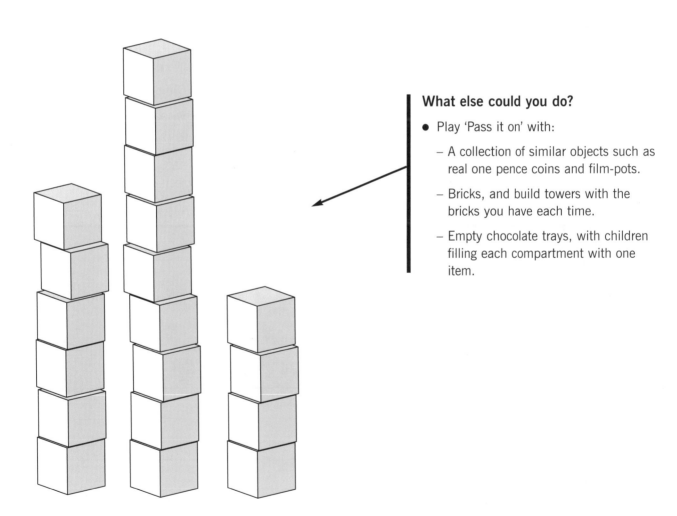

What else could you do?

- Play 'Pass it on' with:

  - A collection of similar objects such as real one pence coins and film-pots.

  - Bricks, and build towers with the bricks you have each time.

  - Empty chocolate trays, with children filling each compartment with one item.

Knock Them Down

Area of Maths:
MAINLY NUMBER AND CALCULATING

Description
Children roll balls at skittles and add up their total 'hits' as their score.

Background

- Giving each child two balls helps them keep track of turn-taking. It also helps if each child's pair is a different colour.

- Marking the original skittle arrangement on the ground helps the setting-up.

- As an independent activity, the learning opportunities are mainly focused on counting and recording totals. If, on later occasions, an adult is present, the children's attention can be drawn to the addition and subtraction by talking about, for example, how many are left, how many they have scored first and then all together.

Working towards these Early Learning Goals

- Count reliably up to ten every-day objects.

- Say and use number names in familiar contexts.

- Recognise numerals 1 to 9.

- Use developing mathematical ideas and methods to solve practical problems.

- Use language such as 'more' or 'less' to compare two numbers.

- In practical activities and discussion, begin to use the vocabulary involved in adding and subtracting.

- Find one more or one less than a number from one to ten.

- Begin to relate addition to combining two groups of objects and subtracting to 'taking away'.

Using these Stepping Stones

- Use mathematical language in play.

- Use some number names accurately in play.

- Separate a group of three or four objects in different ways, beginning to recognise that the total is still the same.

- Count out up to six objects from a larger group.

- Count an irregular arrangement of up to ten objects.

Who is it suitable for?

- A small group outside as free-choice activity.

Prerequisite knowledge and skills

- Counting opportunities to ten.

- Participation in a small group.

Vocabulary

- *one, two, three …, How many …?, count, more, fewer, one more, one less, add, and, make, sum, total, altogether, score, How many are left?, How many have gone?*

28

Knock Them Down

We are going to play skittles and count how many we knocked down

You will need: ten skittles (or plastic bottles containing some sand), two balls for each child (preferably a different colour for each child), chalkboard and chalk or flipchart and pens

Main activity

- Stand the skittles in a four- three- two- one arrangement. Mark the position for each skittle.
- Children take it in turns to roll two balls, one at a time, at the skittles. After each ball they count how many they have knocked down.
- After rolling both their balls, they record their total number of skittles knocked down on the board or flipchart. After each child has rolled their two balls, stand up all the skittles for the next player.
- *How many do you think you will knock down?*
- *Where will you stand to roll?*
- *How many is that all together?*
- *How many are left standing?*
- *What is your score this time? How will you record that?*
- *Show me your best score so far – where did you write that?*
- *How do you know it is that many all together?*

Adaptations

- An easier version is to play with fewer skittles in a three- two- one arrangement.
- Further challenges include:
  - Stand the skittles up after the first ball, the child then holds that score in their head and adds on the skittles knocked down on the second roll.
  - Ask how you could score ten (a 'strike') with two balls.

Does the child ...

- Play co-operatively in a small group?
- Use words such as 'all together', 'that makes', 'more' and 'less' when playing?
- Use some numerals to record the number of fallen skittles?

Pupil page

Knock Them Down

0							
1							
2							
3							
4							
5							
6							
7							
8							
9							
10							

(**Developments**)

Moving on

- Use the recording chart, resource page A, to discuss the game and to compare some of the scores; *Who had a higher (lower) score? Can you see a score of five anywhere? Where are your scores, Katya?*

- Use the experience of 'Knock Them Down' to focus on mentally adding one more: *If Elie knocked down three skittles and then another one, how many did she knock down altogether?* You could also, or instead, combine two small amounts: *Matt knocked down two skittles then another three: how many did he score all together?*

- Invite the children to explain, using words and maybe the skittles themselves, how they worked these out.

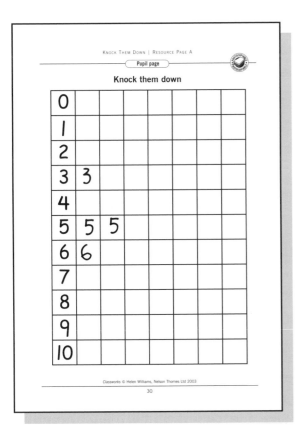

What else could you do?

- Play with different numbers of skittles or with skittle indifferent arrangements – how does this affect the scores?

- Score throws of beanbags into a basket.

- Invite the children to think of their own game to score.

- Introduce a simple group recording grid as shown, where the total score is written in the correct row on the grid.

Listen and Count

Area of Maths:
MAINLY NUMBER

Description

Children listen to some objects being dropped one by one into a container. They say how many they think are in the container before looking and counting.

Background

- These are counting activities for the children that make use of both hearing and sight. It is important that they are given opportunities to count in many different contexts.

- In 'Listen and Count' the children count the sound of counters dropping into a container. It is more difficult to count sounds such as beats on a glockenspiel as there is nothing visible to check, as there is in this activity.

Working towards these Early Learning Goals

- Count reliably up to ten every-day objects.
- Say and use number names in familiar contexts.
- Use language such as 'more' or 'less' to compare two numbers.
- Use developing mathematical ideas and methods to solve practical problems.

Using these Stepping Stones

- Show an interest in numbers and counting.
- Use some number names and number language spontaneously.
- Willingly attempt to count, with some numbers in the correct order.
- Show curiosity about numbers by offering comments or asking questions.
- Count actions or objects that cannot be moved.

Who is it suitable for?

- A large or small group with an adult, and in pairs as a free-choice activity.

Prerequisite knowledge and skills

- Experience of hiding familiar items inside bags or boxes and attempting to identify them by shaking or feeling before looking.
- Opportunities to count small numbers of objects.
- Free play with sound-making rhythm instruments.

Vocabulary

- *one, two, three …, count, How many times?, How many …?, listen, tell me*

Listen and Count

We are going to listen carefully and count how many sounds we hear

You will need: a container, such as a tin or cup, counters or buttons that make a clear sound when dropped into the container

Main activity

- The children cover their eyes as you drop a small number of items such as counters, one at a time, into a tin or cup.

- When you say 'stop', can they say how many they think have been dropped into the tin?

- *What exactly did you hear, Ceri?*

- *That's what you heard, so how many do you think we will see when we tip them out?*

- *Try to count every counter as you hear it drop into the tin.*

- *What do you think, Courtney?*

- *Why do you think that?*

- *How sure are you?*

- *Were we right?*

- Tip them out and ask someone to count them for everyone to see.

Adaptations

- An easier version is to drop the items in a regular rhythm. The listening child drops a similar item into a similar cup to match what they hear.

- Further challenges include:

  – Drop the items irregularly.

  – Ask: *Was that more (less) than last time?*

Does the child ...

- Join in by making comments or asking questions?

- Work effectively for a short while with a partner?

- Count in this context with increasing accuracy?

Developments

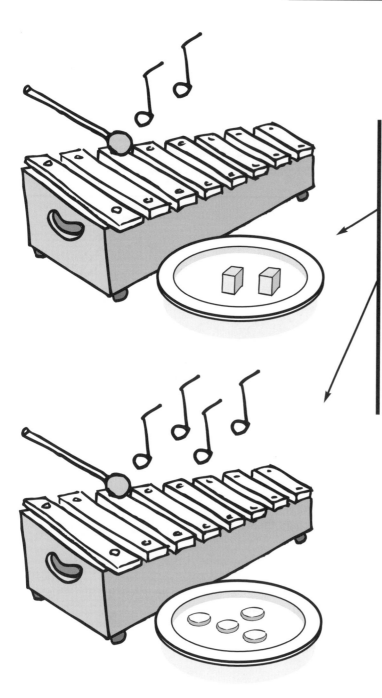

Moving on

- Children can work in pairs repeating and exploring the game. (Expect them to drop in too many to count!)

- Experiment, and encourage them to experiment, by listening to different items being dropped; *can we count something really quiet?*

- Try this: An adult strikes a glockenspiel slowly, a small number of times. Every time the child hears one beat, they place one cube or counter on a dish. *How many beats did you hear?*

- Try varying the speed and regularity of the sounds.

- Encourage the children to invent their own listening and counting challenges.

What else could you do?

- Drop one pence coins into a tin and ask: *How much is in the tin?*

- Play it really loudly!

- Shake a small number of items in a closed pot and ask for 'good guesses' as well as 'silly guesses' of how many are inside.

Match the Dice

Area of Maths:
MAINLY NUMBER AND CALCULATING

Description

'Match the Dice' provides an opportunity to add and subtract in a game context. There are no winners or losers, simply active participants.

Background

- This is quite a sophisticated game involving addition, subtraction and problem-solving. Each time a die is rolled, the child has to decide the appropriate operation and the number to subtract or add. It helps to model the game and talk the operation through, for example: *I have rolled a three, now, I have two on my plate, and I want three ... so I have to add one more to make three.*

- There will be situations where they do nothing, that is when the die-roll already matches the number in their dish. This is worth drawing attention to: *What do you do now, Andrew?*

Working towards these Early Learning Goals

- Count reliably up to ten every-day objects.
- Say and use number names in familiar contexts.
- Use developing mathematical ideas and methods to solve practical problems.
- Use language such as 'more' or 'less' to compare two numbers.
- In practical activities and discussion, begin to use the vocabulary involved in adding and subtracting.
- Find one more or one less than a number from one to ten.
- Begin to relate addition to combining two groups of objects and subtracting to 'taking away'.

Using these Stepping Stones

- Compare two groups of objects, saying when they have the same number.
- Recognise groups with one, two or three objects.
- Show an interest in number problems.
- Sometimes show confidence and offer solutions to problems.
- Use own methods to solve a problem.

Who is it suitable for?

- A small group with an adult.

Prerequisite knowledge and skills

- Using dice as part of a collecting game.
- Counting to at least five.
- Experience of describing what they are doing.

Vocabulary

- *one, two, three ..., How many ...?, count, more, fewer, too many, too few, one more, one less, two more, two less, add, and, take (away), leave, How did you work it out?, What could we try next?*

Match the Dice

We will make the number of counters match the number shown on the die.

You will need: a dish and a one-to-three dot die for each child, a tray of objects such as counters

Main activity

- Give each child a dish and ask them to collect two things each from the central tray. They take it in turns to roll a die.

- They make the number of items in their dish match the number they have rolled. For example, if they have two items in their dish and roll a three, they take one item from the middle to add to their dish to make three altogether; if they roll a one they have to return one item to the middle.

- *You have rolled a ...one. What do you do now?*

- *Will you need to put some in your dish or take some out, this time?*

- *What would happen if you rolled a three?*

- *How did you work out how many to take?*

- *How many dinosaurs are in your dish? What will one more (less) be?*

Adaptations

- An easier version is to begin with each child having a full dish of counters. They take the rolled amount out each time. Being the first to empty your dish means you are the winner.

- Further challenges include:

  – Play with a one-to-six dot die and encourage them to talk about the numbers being subtracted or added each time.

  – Play with a numeral die rather than a spotty one.

Does the child ...

- Work out what they have to do each time?

- Talk about the totals using some addition and subtraction vocabulary?

- Play co-operatively in a small group?

(**Developments**)

Moving on

- What happens if we start with a different number of objects?

- Ask the children for ideas about what they think will happen.

- *What number shall we start with?*

- Try their ideas and discuss what happened.

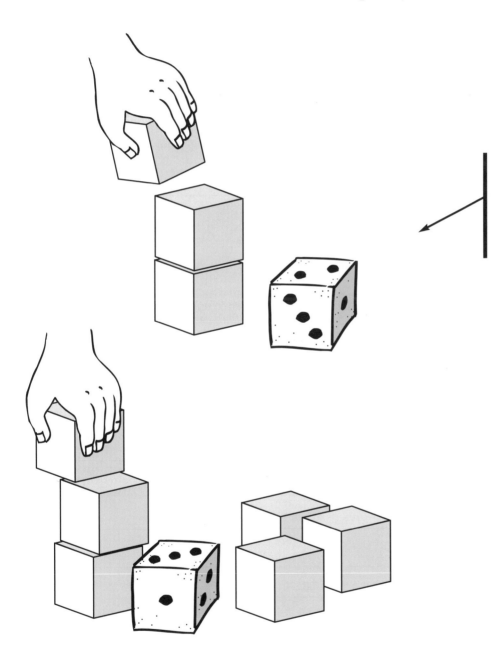

What else could you do?

- Play it big with large items.

- Play with interlocking cubes or bricks, and build towers.

- Play with one pence coins.

In the Bag

Area of Maths:
MAINLY NUMBER

Description

Can the children work out how many items have been added to the bag before the bag is tipped out and checked?

Background

- 'In the Bag' is a counting game that includes some mental work. Children can see one item being dropped into the bag at a time, which, once it is in the bag, they cannot see. They have to use this knowledge to count to a small total in their heads.

- It is important to start at different places in the ring of children each time. This is because it is easier to count the objects sitting opposite, rather than alongside, the action.

- Asking the children how sure they are and how they know, even though we might not get many answers, is an important way of signalling that you want them to become confident in their responses.

Working towards these Early Learning Goals:

- Count reliably up to ten every-day objects.
- Say and use number names in familiar contexts.
- In practical activities and discussion, begin to use the vocabulary involved in adding and subtracting.
- Use developing mathematical ideas and methods to solve practical problems.

Using these Stepping Stones

- Show an interest in numbers and counting.
- Use some number names and number language spontaneously.
- Willingly attempt to count, with some numbers in the correct order.
- Count actions or objects that cannot be moved.
- Say with confidence the number that is one more than a given number.

Who is it suitable for?

- A large or small group sitting in a ring with an adult.

Prerequisite knowledge and skills

- Opportunities to count small numbers of objects.
- Following instructions such as: *Put one thing into the bag and then pass it on.*
- Ability to watch another child doing something and say what they have done.

Vocabulary

- *number, one, two, three ..., How many ...?, count, count on, more, less, fewer, add, make, sum, total, all together, one more, two more*

In the Bag

We are going to watch as the bricks are put into the bag and say how many bricks are in the bag altogether

You will need: a soft bag such as a shoe bag, a collection of bricks or similar, all in one colour and size

Main activity

- Sit in the ring of children and hold the bag. To play, the bag is passed around the ring. Practise doing this.

- Next, each child, on receiving the bag, drops one brick into it before passing it on.

 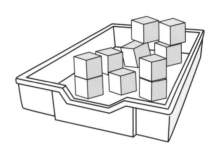

- *Fiona is giving me the bag, now I am picking up one brick and dropping the one brick into the bag. Now I am passing the bag on to Sean.*

- Encourage each child to say what they are doing.

- At an appropriate point, stop the bag's progress.

- *Who knows (can tell us) how many bricks are in the bag, before we tip them out and count them?*

- Children explain how many bricks the bag contains before it is emptied and checked.

- *Who is very (quite) sure how many are in our bag this time?*

- *How do you know, Biniam?*

- *What do you think, Sam?*

- *Why do you think it is that many?*

- *How did you work that out?*

- *Let's start again with an empty bag, this time from Chelsea.*

Adaptations

- An easier version is to use a bag the children can see, to support their mental counting, for example a freezer bag. (This must be supervised by an adult.)

- Further challenges include:

  – *How many will be in the bag by the time it reaches Josh?*

  – Start by counting two or three items in to the bag before passing it around, and count on from there.

Does the child ...

- Engage with and talk about the game?

- State how many are in the bag (correctly or incorrectly)?

- Explain how they reached an answer?

Developments

Moving on

- Can they get better at working out how many are in the bag over a period of time?

- Play the game regularly over a period of time, with different collections of objects, different bags, and a bigger (or smaller) ring of children. Make sure that you start the game with different children, and at different places in the ring. Playing in a group of three or four, with the bag going around more than once, is a new challenge!

- Increasingly draw the children's attention to how they are tackling the problem of counting when they cannot see what to count: *I think you counted all the people, Maria, how did that help?*

- When their confidence has increased, try this: After stopping the bag and tipping out the items, return these to the bag and pass it around a little further, each child dropping one more in, as before. Remind them to 'hold the four in their heads' as they count on.

What else could you do?

- Try it big, with a laundry or carrier bag and large balls, or very small with a jeweller's bag and tiny shells.

- Drop one pence coins into the bag and ask: *How much is in the bag?*

- Do the whole thing in your heads: *Let's pretend we are passing the bag around; Lilly has dropped one brick in, Sasha has dropped one in, and Travis has dropped one in; how many will be in the bag? Let's check.*

- Leave out some cloth bags of bricks for them to feel and count through the material.

Out of the Bag

Area of Maths:
MAINLY NUMBER AND CALCULATING

Description

Can the children work out how many items are left in the bag before the bag is tipped out and checked?

Background

- 'Out of the Bag' is an adaptation of 'In the Bag' (page 38). In this version, the children subtract in ones from five. It helps if they are familiar with 'In the Bag' as counting back is more difficult than counting on.

- This activity is challenging, as the number that is left cannot be seen. (In 'Eating Worms' (page 64) the number that is left is visible.) It is important to start at different places in the ring each time. This is because it is easier to observe sitting opposite, rather than alongside, the action.

- Asking the children how sure they are and how they know, even though we might not get many answers, is an important way of signalling that you want them to become confident in their responses.

Working towards these Early Learning Goals

- Count reliably up to ten every-day objects.

- Say and use number names in familiar contexts.

- In practical activities and discussion, begin to use the vocabulary involved in adding and subtracting.

- Find one more or one less than a number from one to ten.

- Begin to relate addition to combining two groups of objects and subtracting to 'taking away'.

- Use developing mathematical ideas and methods to solve practical problems.

Using these Stepping Stones

- Show an interest in numbers and counting.

- Willingly attempt to count, with some numbers, in the correct order.

- Separate a group of three or four objects in different ways, beginning to recognise that the total is still the same.

- Count actions or objects that cannot be moved.

Who is it suitable for?

- A large or small group sitting in a ring with an adult.

Prerequisite knowledge and skills

- Familiarity with 'In the Bag' (page 38).

- Opportunities to count in many different contexts.

- Ability to watch another child doing something and say what they have done.

Vocabulary

- *one, two, three …, count, more, fewer, one more, How many more?, How many fewer?*

Out of the Bag

We are going to say how many are left in the bag

You will need: a soft bag such as a shoe bag, a collection of bricks or similar, all in one colour and size

Main activity

- Ask the children to sit in a circle. Sit in the ring of children and hold the bag.

- To play, the bag is passed around the ring. Remind them of the game 'In the Bag'. Explain that today we are going to play '**Out** of the Bag'!

- *How do you think we might play '**Out** of the Bag'?*

- Start by counting five bricks into the bag, for everyone to see.

- To play, each child, on receiving the bag, takes one brick out of the bag before passing it on.

- *Fiona is giving me the bag, now I am putting my hand in the bag and taking out one brick. Now I am passing the bag on to Adam.*

- Encourage each child to say what they are doing.

- At an appropriate point, stop the bag's progress and ask: *Who knows (can tell us) how many bricks are left in the bag?*

- Children explain how they work out how many are left in the bag before it is emptied and checked.

- *How many bricks are inside the bag to start?*

- *How many bricks are left in the bag?*

- *Who is very (quite) sure how many are left in our bag now?*

- *How do you know, Selina?*

- *How did you work that out?*

- *Let's start again with a bag of five bricks, this time from Ben.*

Adaptations

- An easier version is to omit the bag and pass around a stick of four cubes, each child removing one each time.

- Further challenges include:

  - *How many will be left in the bag by the time it reaches Rhajid? When will the bag be empty?*

  - Start with more bricks in the bag.

Does the child ...

- Work out how many are left in the bag?

- Talk about the game using some subtraction (addition) vocabulary?

- Explain how they reached an answer?

Developments

Moving on

- Start with six, or another small number of bricks, in the bag. Focus on one amount at a time, and until children are confident at answering the 'how many left' questions.

- Play the game regularly over a period of time, with different collections of objects, different bags, and a bigger or smaller ring of children. Remember to pass it on to a child when it is empty to see if anyone spots there will not be any left to remove!

- Draw the children's attention to how they are working out how many are left each time.

- When their confidence has increased, try this: Start with five bricks in the bag and with each child holding one ball or suitable 'counter'. When the child receives the bag, they take out one brick and put in one ball. Can they talk about what is in the bag, how many bricks and how many balls changed places during the game?

What else could you do?

- Try it big, with a large box in which five children are sitting, or very small, with a matchbox and beads.

- Play with one pence coins and ask: *How much is left?*

- Leave out bags each containing a different five objects. Children work in pairs to count backwards from five.

- Play a hiding game: using bags or boxes of five objects. Take it in turns to remove one, two, three, four, or five (or none) secretly from the box. Ask: *How many are left inside? How do you know?*

In or Out?

Description

A die is rolled to determine how many bricks to add to, or take from, a central pile. The child decides whether to add or take each time. The object is to each build a tower. The children decide how tall their tower is to be.

Background

- This is a comparison and a decision-making game. Initially, it is not important what the end towers look like. What is important is that the children compare tower heights and comment on them, and that they each make their own decision about what to do when it is their turn.

- Decision making is important in mathematics. Here, the child is encouraged to make a decision without repercussions, without being wrong. Later, you can introduce the constraint: each to end with a tower of exactly x bricks.

Working towards these Early Learning Goals

- Count reliably up to ten every-day objects.

- Say and use number names in familiar contexts.

- Use language such as 'more' or 'less' to compare two numbers.

- In practical activities and discussion, begin to use the vocabulary involved in adding and subtracting.

- Use developing mathematical ideas and methods to solve practical problems.

Using these Stepping Stones

- Compare two groups of objects, saying when they have the same number.

- Show an interest in numbers and counting.

- Use some number names and number language spontaneously.

- Show an interest in number problems.

- Recognise groups with one, two or three objects.

- Use own methods to solve a problem.

- Count out up to six objects from a larger group.

Who is it suitable for?

- A small group with an adult.

Prerequisite knowledge and skills

- Free-play with the bricks.

- Opportunities to count small numbers of objects.

- Opportunities to play with and respond to dice.

Vocabulary

- *one, two, three…, How many…?, more, less, fewer, add, and, make, sum, total, altogether, take (away), How many have gone?*

In or Out?

We are going to decide to add more bricks or to take bricks away from our towers

You will need: a large central pile of bricks in one colour and one size, a one-to-three dot die

Main activity

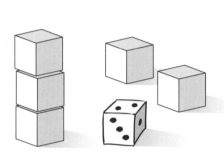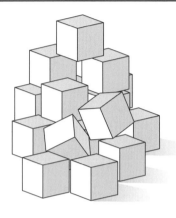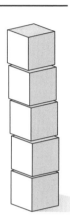

- Start with the children sitting around a central pile of bricks. They each take one brick to start. Taking turns, they roll a one-to-three dot die.

- They look at the number on the die, choosing, and stating, whether to add this number of bricks to their tower, or whether to take this number from their tower and add them to the pile. They compare towers each time.

- *What are you going to do this time, Errol?*

- *What sort of tower do you want to end up with?*

- *Compare with Ricky. Do you have the same number of bricks in your tower?*

- *You have rolled a three. Will you add three cubes onto your tower or take three cubes to add to the pile?*

- *Why did you decide that?*

Adaptations

- An easier version is to ask the children to just add the number rolled in cubes to their tower each time.

- Further challenges include:

  – Playing with bricks of varying sizes.

  – Inviting the child to count their bricks before and after each turn; perhaps they can state what will happen to their total before removing or adding the required number.

Does the child ...

- Engage with and talk about the game?

- Use words such as 'more' and 'less/fewer'?

- Make decisions about whether to add bricks to or take bricks from their tower?

- Count up to three from a larger group?

Developments

Moving on

- Ask the children to recall how the game was played.

- Encourage them to remember and tell us something that happened. Perhaps, for example, they can remember their tower of bricks falling over. When did they decide to stop, and why?

- When (why) did they decide to add bricks to the pile or to their tower?

- What if we each had to end up with a tower exactly five bricks tall?

- Try playing the game with the new rule.

What else could you do?

- Play with apparatus such as Learning Links or Linking Elephants, and choose one colour to add or take each time.

- Play with very large (or very small) bricks and a large (or small) die.

- Play with mixed colours of interlocking cubes.

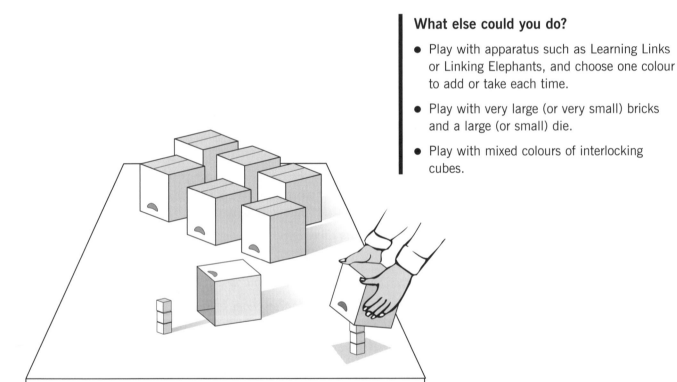

- Hide two towers each of one, two, three and four cubes under similar containers. Lift two containers at a time to find two towers the same.

How Many Hiding?

Area of Maths:
MAINLY NUMBER

Description

In 'How Many Hiding?' children are invited to solve a simple problem: how to make a 'mark' to identify a small amount. This activity works best as an interactive display, when children can return to change and check amounts over a period of time.

Background

- Children are often more accurate when counting if they count things into, and out of, containers. This counting skill can be emphasised during this task.

- 'How Many Hiding?' provides an opportunity for children to read and write symbols and link these to small amounts.

- It is revealing to see how different children tackle this problem. Some might leave an idiosyncratic mark, which may or may not help them identify different containers. Some might use a simple 'tallying' system, with one mark for each item. Some children might use some numerals.

Working towards these Early Learning Goals

- Count reliably up to ten every-day objects.
- Say and use number names in familiar contexts.
- Use language such as 'more' or 'less' to compare two numbers.
- Recognise numerals 1 to 9.
- Use developing mathematical ideas and methods to solve practical problems.

Using these Stepping Stones

- Show an interest in numbers and counting.
- Use some number names and number language spontaneously.
- Show curiosity about numbers by offering comments or asking questions.
- Count up to three or four objects by saying one number name for each item.
- Count an irregular arrangement of up to ten objects.
- Begin to represent numbers using fingers, marks on paper, or pictures.

Who is it suitable for?

- A small group as a free-choice activity.

Prerequisite knowledge and skills

- Experience of hiding familiar items inside bags or boxes and attempting to identify them by shaking or feeling before looking.
- Opportunities to count small numbers of objects.
- Exposure to written numerals.

Vocabulary

- *one, two, three ..., How many ...?, think, imagine, remember, write*

47

How Many Hiding?

We are going to shake the boxes, then peep inside to see how many are hiding

You will need: at least five identical, opaque 'treasure boxes', a number of similar objects to hide inside the containers, for example buttons, teddy-bear counters, play-people, sticky (Post-it) notes, pencils

Main activity

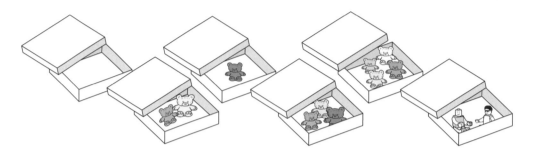

- Display the identical containers. Each container contains between zero and four hidden objects. Provide small sticky (Post-it) notes and pencils.
- *What is hiding in here?*
- *How many are inside this box?*
- Ask the children to start by shaking and peeping in the containers to see how many are hidden inside.
- Next, try remembering which container holds zero, one, two, three or four items without opening the lid first. It's hard, so ask the children to use the sticky notes and pencils to 'leave a message' on each lid to help them remember how many are inside.
- *Can you tell how many are inside here before we peep?*
- *What will you write on the lid?*
- *Can you tell how many are inside by looking at this lid?*
- *Let's muddle the boxes up – can we tell which one is which now?*
- *How do you know?*
- *How sure are you?*

Adaptations

- An easier version is with containers containing up to 3 items.
- Further challenges include:
  – Ask the children to put the containers in order from least to most.
  – Children choose how many to hide in each box.

Does the child ...

- Show some interest in how many/what is hidden?
- Count the items in each container accurately?
- Attempt to record or 'read' small numbers of items?
- Recognise any numerals?

Pupil page

How Many Hiding?

0	1	3	2	4	3
8	6	1	7	8	0
7	2	9	9	0	▢
2	3	4	2	8	5
9	4	9	5	7	2
3	5	6	3	8	4

Classworks © Helen Williams, Nelson Thornes Ltd 2003

Developments

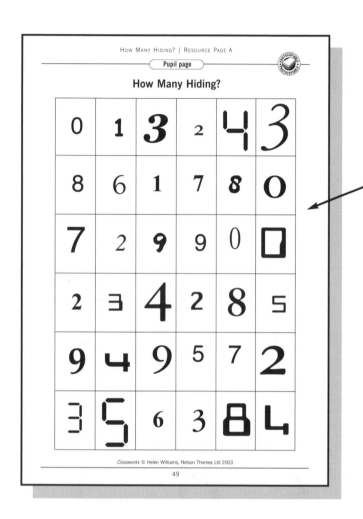

Moving on

- Can the children identify the number of items from the lid-messages on another day?

- Can they identify other children's recordings as well as their own?

- Provide different numerals on paper to tape onto the containers. Make a collection of different numerals for display.

- Have a numeral hunt. Can they find / collect all the different fours... twos ...?

What else could you do?

- Try hiding a different collection of items to record. Ask the children for suggestions.

- Leave messages on envelopes for the numbers of counters inside. Hang these up as a number track.

- Try it big by marking large boxes and hiding children inside.

- Ask the children to label (stock-take) things in the classroom: five pencils, four chairs, parking for three bikes, and so on.

Hidden Dinosaurs

Area of Maths:
MAINLY NUMBER

Description

Small numbers of objects are hidden under cups.
Children have to find cups hiding the same number.

Background

- This is an adaptation of the familiar 'Pairs' game. You may wish to familiarise the children with this new game by playing the matching version, with children lifting cups to find a matching pair of items, such as two beads, or two pegs.

- Play 'Hidden dinosaurs' with a variety of resources to practise making number comparisons in different contexts.

Working towards these Early Learning Goals

- Count reliably up to ten every-day objects.
- Say and use number names in familiar contexts.
- Use developing mathematical ideas and methods to solve practical problems.
- Use language such as 'more' or 'less' to compare two numbers.

Using these Stepping Stones

- Show an interest in numbers and counting.
- Use some number names and number language spontaneously.
- Compare two groups of objects, saying when they have the same number.
- Show curiosity about numbers by offering comments or asking questions.
- Recognise groups with one, two or three objects.
- Count up to three or four objects by saying one number name for each item.

Who is it suitable for?

- A small group with an adult.

Prerequisite knowledge and skills

- Familiarity with matching pairs game.
- Counting up to three items.

Vocabulary

- *one, two, three …, How many …?, more, less, fewer, compare, is the same as, match*

Hidden Dinosaurs

We are going to find matching numbers of counters

You will need: dinosaur counters (or similar) and at least 12 cups big enough to cover up to three of the counters

Main activity

- A number of groups of one, two, and three dinosaurs are hidden under cups. Children take it in turns to lift two cups. If the number of dinosaurs under the two cups are the same, they win the dinosaurs.

- If they are different, replace the cups for someone else.

- *Which two cups are you going to choose?*

- *Will you lift them up one at a time?*

- *Do you have the same number under each cup?*

- *How do you know?*

- *Are you sure?*

- *What do you do now (next)?*

Adaptations

- An easier version is to hide sticks of interlocking cubes, all of the same colour, and allow children to compare the lengths.

- Further challenges include:

  – Score a point (or a dinosaur) for each correct guess. Try to each score five points.

  – Increase the number hidden under the cups.

Does the child ...

- Recognise up to three items without counting?

- Use words such as 'more' or 'less' when playing?

- Use number names confidently?

Developments

Moving on

- Discuss the children's experiences of playing the game.

- What did they enjoy about it?

- Compare ways of working out if the amount under the two cups is the same.

- Leave out the materials for them to experiment with the game.

- Encourage them to teach the game to someone else.

What else could you do?

- Change the hidden items, play it big outside as well as on the table top.

- Hide different items in a variety of sizes, for example one large shell and two conkers, one play-person and two counters, and so on. Can the child still recognise the two different groups as '3'?

- Hide one pence, two pence and five pence coins and find matching pairs under the cups.

3

3

Gold Up

Area of Maths:
MAINLY NUMBER

Description

'Gold Up' makes use of dried butter beans, sprayed gold on one side, to practise counting and comparing small amounts in a game context. There are no winners or losers, simply active participants.

Background

- Without progressing onto the recording stage, 'Gold Up' is a simple counting and comparison game.

- Because there are five beans, each with an equal chance of landing with gold side up, the probability is that there will be more twos and threes spilled than zeros, ones, fours and fives. Try ten beans to spill more fives!

- Once the children are confident with the game, introducing the recording grids moves the game onto a higher thinking level. The completed recording grids demonstrate that some numerals occur more frequently than others, providing opportunities for discussion and prediction.

Working towards these Early Learning Goals

- Count reliably up to ten every-day objects.
- Say and use number names in familiar contexts.
- Use language such as 'more' or 'less' to compare two numbers.
- Use developing mathematical ideas and methods to solve practical problems.
- Recognise numerals 1 to 9.

Using these Stepping Stones

- Show an interest in numbers and counting.
- Use some number names and number language spontaneously.
- Use some number names accurately in play.
- Separate a group of three or four objects in different ways, beginning to recognise that the total is still the same.
- Show curiosity about numbers by offering comments or asking questions.
- Count out up to six objects from a larger group.
- Begin to represent numbers using fingers, marks on paper, or pictures.

Who is it suitable for?

- A small group working independently.

Prerequisite knowledge and skills

- Opportunities to handle a tray of dried butter beans.
- Experience of taking a turn in a game.
- Experience of counting up to five objects.

Vocabulary

- *one, two, three ..., more, fewer, How many ...?, count, group, How many more?*

Gold Up

We are going to count how many beans land gold up

You will need: a small bag of five dried butter beans, painted or sprayed gold on one side, and a paper plate, (one per child)
For 'Moving on': pencils (preferably gold) and lots of copies of resource page A (cut into two)

Main activity

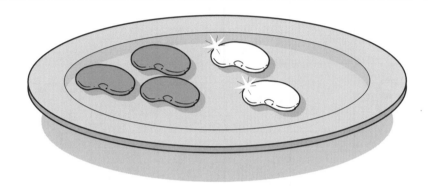

- Model shaking five beans in your two cupped hands and spilling them onto your plate. Count the number that land gold side up. Repeat this a number of times, encouraging the children to count and discuss the number of gold-up beans each time.

- Children then play in pairs with their own beans, taking it in turns to spill and count their gold-up beans.

- *How many are 'gold-up' this time?*

- *Whose turn is it?*

- *What happened that time?*

- *Did you spill more (less) gold this time?*

- *How many do you think you might spill next time?*

- *How many gold beans is that?*

Adaptations

- An easier version is to with three or four gold beans.

- Further challenges include:

  - Play with up to ten beans.

  - Each player has to say whether they think their partner will spill more, or fewer, beans next turn.

Does the child ...

- Work confidently with a partner?

- Attempt to count the gold beans, with some accuracy?

- Comment on totals by making comparisons, for example: 'Look, I've got four this time'.

Gold Up

0							
1							
2							
3							
4							
5							

0							
1							
2							
3							
4							
5							

Developments

Moving on

- Ask the children to recall how the game was played.

- Encourage them to remember and tell us something that happened; for example, perhaps they can remember spilling no (or all) gold.

- Introduce a simple recording grid as on resource page A. Model using this. When you spill and count your gold beans, you write the number of gold beans in the correct row on the grid.

0							
I	I	I					
2	2	2	2	2			
3	3	3					
4							
5							

0	o						
I	I	I	I	I			
2	2	2	2	2	2	2	2
3	3	3	3	3	3		
4	4	4	4				
5	5	5					

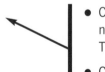

- Children replay the game, recording their number of gold beans on their grids. They will use a lot of grids.

- Collect the grids for comparison and discussion at a suitable time.

What else could you do?

- *What happens if we play and record 'White Side Up' instead of 'Gold Up'?*

- Encourage the children to decide when they have completed a grid. Is it when one number reaches the 'finish line'? Or is it when all the squares have numerals written inside? Any other ideas?

- What else would they like to try?

Gold Up (2)

Area of Maths:
MAINLY NUMBER AND CALCULATING

Description

'Gold Up (2)' makes use of dried butter beans, sprayed gold on one side, to represent the pairs of numbers that make a total of five.

Background

- 'Gold Up (2)' extends 'Gold Up' (page 54) from counting into calculating.

- This is an example of 'partitioning' an amount into its complements (or number pairs) *see also* 'Eating Worms' (page 64) and 'Under the Box' (page 7).

- Keeping the total constant each time the game is played encourages children to calculate in their heads. Working in pairs and making each child tell their partner the number of gold beans they see helps internalisation of combinations that make five.

- Over time you can extend this activity to working with the complements of numbers up to ten.

Working towards these Early Learning Goals

- Count reliably up to ten every-day objects.

- Say and use number names in familiar contexts.

- Use developing mathematical ideas and methods to solve practical problems.

- Use language such as 'more' or 'less' to compare two numbers.

- In practical activities and discussion, begin to use the vocabulary involved in adding and subtracting.

- Begin to relate addition to combining two groups of objects and subtracting to 'taking away'.

Using these Stepping Stones

- Show an interest in numbers and counting.

- Use some number names and number language spontaneously.

- Separate a group of three or four objects in different ways, beginning to recognise that the total is still the same.

- Show curiosity about numbers by offering comments or asking questions.

- Count an irregular arrangement of up to ten objects.

Who is it suitable for?

- Pairs of children working independently.

Prerequisite knowledge and skills

- Familiarity with the 'Gold Up' counting game (page 54).

- Confidence in counting, and recognising groups of up to five items.

Vocabulary

- *one, two, three ..., How many ...?, more, fewer, one more, two more, one fewer, two fewer, group, set, count*

Gold Up (2)

We are going to say how many beans are white and how many are gold each time

You will need: a small bag of five dried butter beans, painted or sprayed gold on one side, and a paper plate (for every child)

Main activity

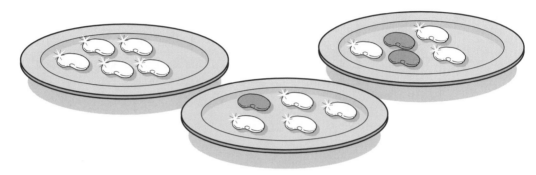

- Children work in pairs, taking it in turns to shake their five beans in cupped hands and spill them onto their plate. Out loud, they say how many of their beans are gold-side up, and then how many are white-side up.

- As they play, encourage them to check each other's, and to say 'five altogether' each time.

I've got 4 golds and 1 white

I've got 3 golds and 2 whites

- *How many beans are you playing with (today)?*

Five altogether!

- *What happened that time?*
- *Did you spill more (less) gold this time?*
- *If you have three gold, how many white will there be?*
- *How many beans is that all together?*

Adaptations

- An easier version is with four beans.
- Further challenges include:
  - Find a way of recording the number of gold and white each throw.
  - *What if we play with six beans? What numbers of gold beans can we get each time?*

Does the child ...

- Work with their partner, taking turns and responding to both their throws?
- Recognise amounts of up to five without counting?
- Compare two groups and say which is more?

(**Developments**)

Moving on

- After the children have explored spilling five beans in pairs, ask them what they noticed about the numbers of beans each time.

- Talk about the pairs of numbers. Ask questions like: *If you had three gold beans, Justin, how many white beans did you have?*

- Encourage them to explain their answers.

- *What happens if* … Invite them to choose a different small number of beans to try next time.

What else could you do?

- Repeat the game with beans sprayed with a different colour, or on a larger scale with bean bags with a spot on one side.

- *What if we played the same game with coins and counted the heads and the tails each time?*

- Relate this game to 'Under the Box' (page 7).

Fish for Treasure

Description

Children 'fish' for, and count, items of treasure hidden in dry sand.

Background

- Vary the items you use to play this game. Ask the children for suggestions of what to hide and find.
- Try hiding lots of the same items, for example coins, as well as a variety of items.
- Give children experience of counting very small items such as sequins, as well as much larger items in the outside sand pit.
- It is not necessary to move too quickly to the recording (see 'Moving on').

Working towards these Early Learning Goals

- Count reliably up to ten every-day objects.
- Say and use number names in familiar contexts.
- Use language such as 'more' or 'less' to compare two numbers.
- Use developing mathematical ideas and methods to solve practical problems.

Using these Stepping Stones

- Use mathematical language in play.
- Show an interest is numbers and counting.
- Use some number names and number language spontaneously.
- Willingly attempt to count, with some numbers in the correct order.
- Show curiosity about numbers by offering comments or asking questions.
- Count an irregular arrangement of up to ten objects.

Who is it suitable for?

- A small group as a free-choice/independent activity.

Prerequisite knowledge and skills

- Opportunities to use dice as part of a game.
- Counting experiences to five.
- Free sand play.

Vocabulary

- *one, two, three …, How many more to make …?, more, fewer, count*

Fish for Treasure

We are going to roll the die and fish for that many pieces of treasure

You will need: tray(s) of dry sand, pieces of 'treasure' (such as beads, coins and jewels), sieves or tea strainers, one-to-three dot dice, bags for found treasure

Main activity

- Hide some treasure in the sand and give each child a sieve or tea strainer and a collecting bag.
- Children roll the die and fish for that amount of treasure.
- *Let's use the sieves to find some treasure.*
- *What do you think is hiding in here?*
- *What treasure do you think you will find?*
- *How many are you fishing for?*
- *How many is that (so far)?*
- *How many more do you need?*

Adaptations

- An easier version is to omit the dice. Children fish for and count the pieces of treasure caught.
- Further challenges include:
  - *How much treasure have you caught altogether?*
  - Try rolling a one-to-six die and finding that much treasure.

Does the child ...

- Recognise the die dot numbers?
- Engage in the game, contributing comments and asking questions?
- Use words such as 'more', 'lots' and 'less'?

Developments

Moving on

- Invite the children to talk about their treasure-hunting experiences.

- Model the following game for the children to play in pairs: one child writes a numeral on a piece of card, the other child has to find that number of items. Swap roles.

- This could develop into one child choosing a number of items to hide in the sand. They record this number and their partner must find them all.

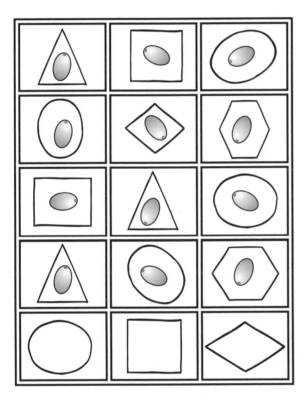

What else could you do?

- Bury large items in wet sand outside, and use your hands.

- Float 'fish' in the water tray and catch them with sieves.

- Give each child a chocolate-box tray to fill with found treasure, one piece in each compartment, and encourage discussion about how many they have found and how many are left to find.

Eating Worms

Area of Maths:
MAINLY NUMBER AND CALCULATING

Description

In 'Eating Worms', children work in pairs to practise subtracting small amounts from five in a story-telling context.

Background

- It is important to keep the total number of 'worms' constant each time this is played. This allows the children to calculate in their heads, rather than simply counting how many are left each time.

- In 'Eating Worms' the children can see the worms that are left. As they grow more confident, encourage them to subtract mentally first – to say how many are left before counting to check.

- Repeating this activity in different contexts helps children internalise the calculations. Remember to point out similarities so they don't just think it is a new experience!

Working towards these Early Learning Goals

- Count reliably up to ten every-day objects.
- Say and use number names in familiar contexts.
- Use developing mathematical ideas and methods to solve practical problems.
- In practical activities and discussion, begin to use the vocabulary involved in adding and subtracting.
- Find one more or one less than a number from one to ten.
- Begin to relate addition to combining two groups of objects and subtracting to 'taking away'.

Using these Stepping Stones

- Show an interest in numbers and counting.
- Use some number names and number language spontaneously.
- Show curiosity about numbers by offering comments or asking questions.
- Show an interest in number problems.
- Sometimes show confidence and offer solutions to problems.
- Use own methods to solve a problem.

Who is it suitable for?

- A large or small group with an adult, and later as a free-choice activity in pairs.

Prerequisite knowledge and skills

- Counting backwards in ones, by 'taking away' from a small amount.
- Ability to watch and describe what they see happening.
- Recognition of small amounts.

Vocabulary

- *zero, one, two, three ..., how many ...? count, more, fewer, how many are left?, how many have gone?*

Eating Worms

We are going to feed worms to a fish, and count how many worms are left

You will need: fish photocopied onto card from resource page A with a slot cut in their mouths, strips of five worms, each photocopied onto card from resource page B (all per pair)

Main activity

- Cut a slot in the fish's mouth. Look at the fish and the worms together. Establish there are five worms altogether on each strip. Children watch as you 'feed' the strip of card worms to the fish through the slot. Describe what is happening.

- *The fish is really hungry today, he is going to eat three worms ... watch ... here they go ... one disappears, two disappear, three disappear. Who can tell me how many worms are left to eat?*

- Repeat with a fresh strip of worms.

- Children work in pairs, feeding their fish and describing how many are left to eat.

- *How many worms are (were) there altogether?*

- *How many will this fish eat this time?*

- *How many have disappeared (been eaten)?*

- *How many are left (still to be eaten)?*

- *How can you work out how many are left?*

Adaptations

- An easier version is to use strips of three or four worms.

- Further challenges include:

  - *What would happen if we started with ... six (or more) worms?*

  - *How can you work out how many are left before you look and check?*

Does the child ...

- Work out how many are left each time?

- Talk about the game using some addition and subtraction vocabulary?

- Work confidently and appropriately in a pair?

Pupil page

Eating Worms

Eating Worms

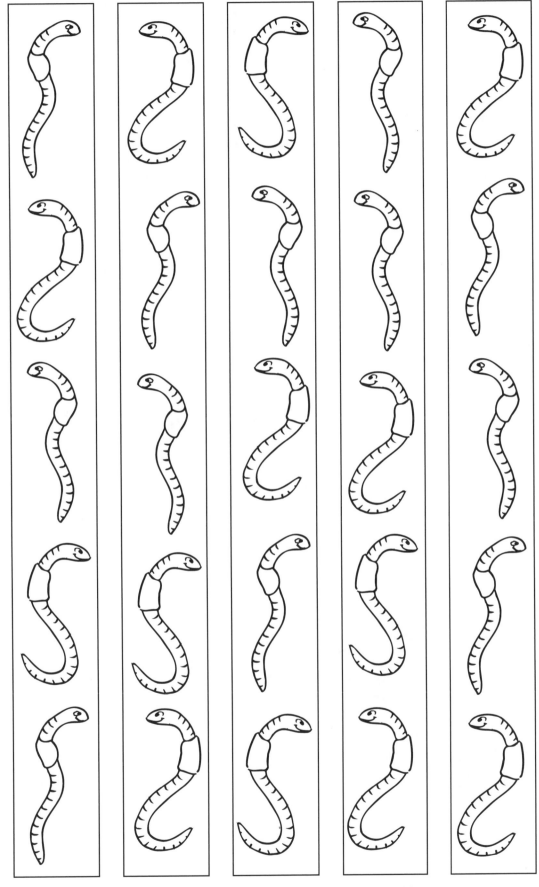

Developments

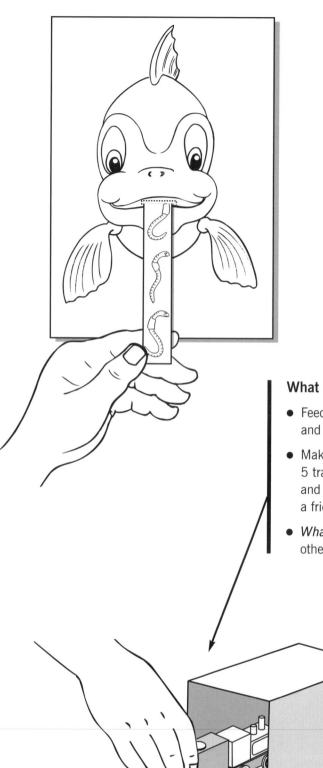

Moving on

- After plenty of opportunities to feed the fish, have a group discussion focusing on the numbers involved: *When one worm was eaten, how many were left for the fish to eat? What about when the fish ate three worms?*

- Invite the children to say how sure they are; quite sure or very sure? They should describe and explain their answers.

- Change the number of worms the fish is fed on different occasions.

What else could you do?

- Feed all sorts of things, for example make a 'box monster', and feed them biscuits.

- Make some card 'tunnels', each big enough to hide up to 5 train carriages. Children drive their trains around the track and into the tunnel, hiding different numbers of carriages for a friend to work out how many are in the tunnel.

- *What would happen if ...?* Challenge the children to think of other taking away games to play.

Counting Puppet

Area of Maths:
MAINLY NUMBER

Description

A puppet is used to illustrate some counting errors, which children correct.

Background

- The counting puppet can become a regular feature of the numerate classroom. It is a powerful learning tool because it helps children focus on the processes and skills of counting accurately. It also places the child in the position of teacher and knowledge-holder.

- It is important to start with familiar counting objects, in order to relate the activity as closely as possible to the children's experiences. The range of counting contexts can be varied as the children's confidence grows.

- As you control the puppet, describe what s/he is doing as a commentary, or try saying the puppet's thoughts aloud. This helps children 'read' the situation.

Working towards these Early Learning Goals

- Count reliably up to ten every-day objects.
- Say and use number names in familiar contexts.
- Use developing mathematical ideas and methods to solve practical problems.

Using these Stepping Stones

- Use mathematical language in play.
- Show an interest in numbers and counting.
- Use some number names and number language spontaneously.
- Willingly attempt to count, with some numbers in the correct order.
- Show curiosity about numbers by offering comments or asking questions.
- Show increased confidence with numbers by spotting errors.
- Begin to count beyond ten.

Who is it suitable for?

- A large or small group with an adult.

Prerequisite knowledge and skills

- A variety of opportunities to count amounts.
- Ability to watch another child doing something and say what they have done.

Vocabulary

- *one, two, three ..., count, right, wrong, How did you work it out?*

Counting Puppet

We are going to help someone to learn how to count

You will need: a hand puppet and a tray of familiar counting items such as bricks

Main activity

- Introduce the puppet as someone who is just learning to count.

- *S/he has come to us for some help as s/he keeps making mistakes and has heard we are all very good at counting.*

- The puppet lines up a maximum of ten objects to count. As the puppet counts the items, make a common counting error, such as missing an item, or reciting the numbers out of order. Children try to spot the error and correct it.

- *Can you help (puppet name)?*

- *Can you say what s/he should do, Kirsten?*

- *What happened, Ryan? What did you see happen?*

- *What do you want to say to (puppet name)?*

Adaptations

- An easier version is to keep the number of items low and repeat the same error a number of times.

- Further challenges include:

  – Ask a child to count the items correctly after the error has been corrected.

  – Ask a child to describe what the puppet does as they do it.

Does the child ...

- Comment on what they see the puppet do?

- Notice or correct any counting errors?

- Show a high level of involvement?

Developments

Moving on

- Leave the puppet and counting items out for the children to play with.

- Over time, the puppet can 'learn' how to successfully deal with an earlier error – although they will need to be reminded before they start counting.

- The range of errors the puppet makes can be extended to match relevant teaching points such as:

  - Saying two numbers whilst touching one object.

  - Remembering to stop at the appropriate point when counting out a small amount from a larger collection.

  - Organising the collection in order to count the objects easily.

  - Knowing where to start and stop – place the items in a circle.

  - Remembering the correct number to name the whole group when the count is completed.

  - Counting the same items twice and not reaching two different conclusions.

What else could you do?

- Provide a set of hand puppets and counting resources for the children to play with in pairs.

- Vary the items to count: make them very small or very large, or all different types.

- Make errors when counting in different contexts, such as counting moves along a track, or beats of a drum.

Ten Bits

Area of Maths:
MAINLY NUMBER

Description

Children make Lego models, each using exactly ten pieces.

Background

- This activity develops 'Use Them All' (page 1).

- This is a problem-solving task: *How will you make sure the models have ten, and only ten, bricks?* Noting what different children do, as well as providing opportunities to discuss how different children tackled the task, helps establish that you value processes as well as results.

- Some children will find it difficult to keep the number of bricks to ten, and will want to add more bricks to make their model more attractive. It can help to start with all the same shape and colour of brick, later repeating the activity with a range of bricks. This can help children focus on the number, rather than the attributes of the bricks, and to compare the models afterwards.

Working towards these Early Learning Goals

- Count reliably up to ten every-day objects.
- Say and use number names in familiar contexts.
- Use developing mathematical ideas and methods to solve practical problems.
- Use language such as 'more' or 'less' to compare two numbers.
- In practical activities and discussion, begin to use the vocabulary involved in adding and subtracting.

Using these Stepping Stones

- Show an interest in number and counting.
- Use some number names and number language spontaneously.
- Show an interest in number problems.
- Show curiosity about numbers by offering comments or asking questions.
- Count an irregular arrangement of up to ten objects.
- Sometimes show confidence and offer solutions to problems.
- Use own methods to solve a problem.

Who is it suitable for?

- A small group working independently.

Prerequisite knowledge and skills

- Counting to ten.
- Experience of 'Use Them All' (page 1).

Vocabulary

- *one, two, three ..., how many ...?, more, fewer, altogether, count, How many more to make ...?, make, build, draw*

Ten Bits

> We are going to use ten bricks to make a model

You will need: Lego, or similar construction toy, and a small baseboard (one per child)

Main activity

- Provide a tray of Lego, or a similar construction toy, and give each child a baseboard to build on.
- Ask the children to build a model using only ten pieces of Lego.
- Observe how they tackle the task.
- *How are you going to make sure you have only ten pieces?*
- *Do you have enough?*
- *What are you going to do now (next)?*
- *What are you making?*
- *What have you made with your ten bricks?*
- *How can you check that you have used the right amount?*

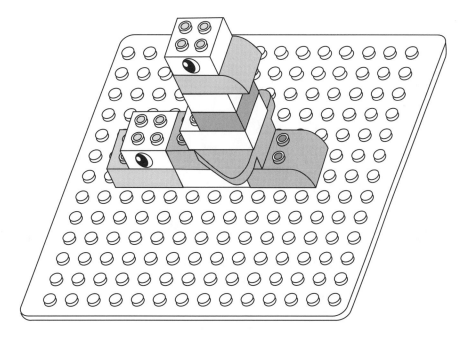

Adaptations

- An easier version is to use five pieces of Lego.
- Further challenges include:
  - *Make a different model using ten pieces.*
  - *Draw what you have made, showing all ten pieces in your drawing.*

Does the child ...

- Make a model with the required number of pieces?
- Tackle the task systematically, keeping track of how many s/he has used?
- Count out the bricks before starting?

(**Developments**)

Moving on

- Display all the 'Ten Bit' models and discuss and compare them. *Do they all 'look like ten'?*

- Invite the children to choose a model to talk about.

- Ask the creator to describe how they solved the problem of making it with ten bricks: *How did you make sure you hadn't used too many?*

- Compare different children's ways of solving the problem.

- Ask the children to choose a new number of bricks to use to make a model. They could work in pairs.

- Encourage them to count out the chosen number of bricks before they start building.

- They match the correct numeral to their completed models.

What else could you do?

- Use different materials; for example, ten shapes to make a picture, ten beads to make a necklace, and so on.

- Have a 'ten' display.

- Ask the children to invent ideas of what to create that shows ten.

The Three Bears

Area of Maths:
MEASURES: LENGTH

Description

Children distinguish between three different lengths by touching Cuisenaire rods.

Background

- This activity uses a familiar story as a context for discussing and comparing three different lengths. Familiarity helps the children cope with the abstraction of wooden rods representing bears. Try saying: *Let's pretend one rod is Daddy bear.*

- A range of length vocabulary can be used; for example, when the rods are upright, words like 'tall' and 'taller', and when lying down, 'long' and 'longer'.

- You might expect some children to select a longer rod for Daddy, a shorter rod for Baby and a middle-sized rod for Mummy. Something different may happen, however, and the key point is that each child makes their own selection and is encouraged to talk about it. The first time you play, it might be enough for children to choose their three rods and talk about the different families, holding up each 'bear' as you call them out; the story can be introduced at a later session.

- Two skills are being emphasised in 'The Three Bears': touch (rather than the more common sight) to identify length; and listening for and acting on key words (Mummy bear, and so on). If you are unsure whether individual children are identifying the correct length of rod by touch, try telling some of the story where they can all see what rod they are choosing.

Working towards these Early Learning Goals

- Use language such as 'greater', 'smaller', 'heavier' or 'lighter' to compare quantities.
- Use developing mathematical ideas and methods to solve practical problems.
- Use every-day words to describe position.

Using these Stepping Stones

- Use mathematical language in play.
- Use size language such as 'big' and 'little'.
- Show interest by sustained construction activity or by talking about shapes or arrangements.
- Show curiosity and observation by talking about shapes, how they are the same or why some are different.
- Order two items by length or height.
- Order two or three items by length.

Who is it suitable for?

- A group with an adult, all sitting in a ring on the floor.

Prerequisite knowledge and skills

- Familiarity with the story of 'The Three Bears'.
- Opportunities to explore freely the tray of Cuisenaire rods.

Vocabulary

- *compare, length, height, long, short, tall, longer, shorter, taller, higher, longest, shortest, tallest, highest*

The Three Bears

We are going to choose some number rods and talk about how tall they are

You will need: a tray of Cuisenaire (number) rods, a story book copy of 'The Three Bears' (optional)

Main activity

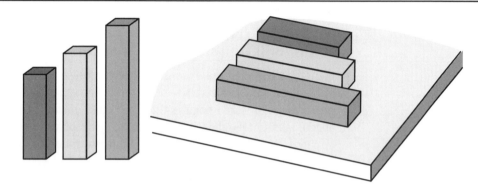

- Remind the children of the tale of 'The Three Bears'. Each child selects one rod to represent Daddy bear, one rod to represent Mummy bear and one rod to represent Baby bear. They hide the three bear-rods behind their backs, or in their laps.

- Tell the story of the three bears. When they hear you say 'Daddy bear', the children hold up their Daddy bear rods, when they hear 'Mummy bear', they hold up their Mummy bear rods and when they hear 'Baby bear' they hold up their Baby bear rods.

- *Look at your family of bears – which bear is this one, Nicole?*

- *Do you see anyone with the same bears as you have chosen?*

- *Tell us about how tall each of your bears are.*

- *How did you know that was Daddy bear, Jamil?*

- *Are you sure that is Baby bear? How do you know?*

- *Who is left behind your back?*

Adaptations

- An easier version is to lay their family of three rods out for them to see.
- Further challenges include:
  - Select three bears from rods one to five, or six to ten. (Finer comparisons are then necessary.)
  - Record the three rods to remember which you chose for which bear on another occasion.

Does the child ...

- Choose three rods and explain their choice?
- Compare the lengths/heights of 3 (or more) rods and use words like 'long', 'tall', 'short' or 'middle-sized'?
- Select the appropriate rod by feeling?

The Three Bears

Developments

Moving on

- Leave out the rods, the story book and other props for children to play independently.

- Repeat the activity, inviting a child to help retell the story, this time choosing three different rods for each bear.

- Play again another day, asking the children if they can remember which rods they chose for which bear, and why.

What else could you do?

- Tell the story and hide three Compare bears.

- Try using three different lengths of wool or ribbon. (Is this harder or easier? Why?)

- Try the same activity using the 'Three Billy Goats Gruff' as the story.

- *Do we know any other stories with a big, middle-sized and a small character?*

Heavy Shopping

Area of Maths:
MEASURES: WEIGHT AND SOME NUMBER

Description

This activity uses the picture book, 'The Shopping Basket' by John Burningham (Red Fox, 2000), to introduce vocabulary associated with comparing weights.

Background

- Children first use descriptive words such as 'heavy' and later, 'light'. In addition, this activity provides opportunities for the development of comparative language such as 'heavier **than**' and 'lighter **than**'.

- Putting objects into bags to compare their weight helps children pay attention to how they feel rather than how they look. Closing our eyes adds an extra challenge (try it yourself!). Physical experiences of this sort (and that of 'Sandy Socks' page 98) are an important precursor to using a weighing instrument such as balances (see 'Stretchy Scales' page 107 and 'Treasure Hunt' page 118).

- 'Heavy Shopping' uses the same story book ('The Shopping Basket' by John Burningham) as a context for some mathematics as 'Steven's Shopping' (page 16).

Working towards these Early Learning Goals

- Use language such as 'greater', 'smaller', 'heavier' or 'lighter' to compare quantities.
- Use developing mathematical ideas and methods to solve practical problems.
- Count reliably up to ten every-day objects.
- Say and use number names in familiar contexts.

Using these Stepping Stones

- Use mathematical language in play.
- Use size language such as 'big' and 'little'.
- Order two items by weight and capacity.
- Count an irregular arrangement of up to ten objects.

Who is it suitable for?

- A small group with an adult.

Prerequisite knowledge and skills

- Familiarity with the story.
- Role-play experiences involving "shopping"; filling and emptying bags.

Vocabulary

- *measure, size, compare, weight, weights, heavy, light, heavier, lighter, heaviest, lightest*

Heavy Shopping

We are going to talk about how heavy or light a shopping bag is

You will need: the picture book, 'The Shopping Basket' by John Burningham (Red Fox, 2000), a shopping bag containing shopping items from the book: six eggs, five bananas, four apples, three oranges, two doughnuts and one packet of crisps, empty shopping bags – of similar size if possible, gift bags are ideal

Main activity

- After reading the story together, look at the bag of shopping items. Sort them out.

- Children hold a shopping bag by the handles and close their eyes as items of shopping are placed in it one at a time. Encourage them to talk about what they can feel happening.

- When they have tried feeling the bag get heavier, they close their eyes as items are removed one at a time.

- They can try this in pairs.

- *How does the bag feel, Alicia?*

- *What can you feel me doing, Grant?*

- *Does the bag feel heavier or lighter now?*

- *What about now?*

- *Why do you think that was an orange that time?*

- *How can you tell when I take something out?*

- *What are you going to try now?*

Adaptations

- An easier version is to use lots of items of the same type, for example, all oranges or bananas. Make sure the items are quite heavy. You might choose to start with eyes open.

- Further challenges include:

  – Use lighter items, for example packets of crisps: can the children tell when these are added or removed?

  – One child closes their eyes and holds a bag containing some shopping. A second child secretly chooses whether to add an item to, or remove one from the bag. The first child has to say what they have done and how they know.

Does the child ...

- Show some understanding of 'light' as well as 'heavy'?

- Use comparative words like 'lighter' and 'heavier'?

- Identify correctly when the weight has altered?

Developments

Moving on

- Leave out shopping bags of different sizes and shopping items with which to fill them.

- After every child has had plenty of opportunities to explore making up bags of shopping, rehearse the appropriate language with them.

- Model holding two bags by the handles, one in each hand. Ask a child to place shopping items in one bag and 'act' the bag getting heavier, encouraging the children to describe what they see. Ask a second child to add items to the second bag, and act the bags becoming equal in weight.

- Children play with this idea in pairs.

What else could you do?

- Use different items of shopping – ask children for suggestions, perhaps tins or boxes of food.

- Collect empty food-boxes (small cereal packets are ideal) and fill them up to make different weights for children to shop for.

- Put some scoops and small paper-bags into the sand-tray and make 'sand bags' to compare.

Belts

Area of Maths:
MEASURES:
LENGTH

Description

Children cut lengths of coloured paper to make belts for toys.

Background

- In 'Belts' children cut a length of paper to match or fit a space. This is harder than matching two ready cut lengths (see 'Strings' page 110).

- Commonly, children cut off too much, or cut from both ends. Encourage them to hold one end and to cut off all the overlap from the other end, then recheck the length. Expect some mistakes!

- All measurement is to some degree inaccurate. The degree of accuracy that is acceptable varies according to the context. Here, children might have a tight or loose belt, what is important is the experience of measuring, making a decision about the required length and the use of a range of language. If you are lucky, the question of leaving some overlap to 'do up' the belt might arise with some children. You can then discuss how much overlap to leave to make the belt 'work'.

- Displaying the toys with their completed belts provides an opportunity for children to revisit the task, to compare lengths of different belts and to rematch belts to toys.

Working towards these Early Learning Goals

- Use language such as 'greater', 'smaller', 'heavier' or 'lighter' to compare quantities.
- Use developing mathematical ideas and methods to solve practical problems.

Using these Stepping Stones

- Use size language such as 'big' and 'little'.
- Use mathematical language in play.
- Adapt shapes or cut material to size.

Who is it suitable for?

- A small group with an adult helper; later as an independent task.

Prerequisite knowledge and skills

- Recognises longer and shorter when comparing two different lengths.
- Experience of finding matching lengths (as in 'Strings' page 110).

Vocabulary

- *measure, size, guess, estimate, enough, not enough, too much, too little, nearly, close to, about the same as, just over, just under, longer, shorter*

Belts

We are going to make a belt the correct length for our toy

You will need: strips of coloured paper, in various lengths, all too long for the toys' 'middles', a collection of character toys – none too small, scissors, colouring pens

Main activity

- Introduce the activity by talking about belts. Is anyone wearing one? Why?
- Provide strips of different coloured paper, in different thicknesses and lengths.
- Invite the children to cut the strip to the correct length to make a belt to fit a toy they choose.
- The belts can be decorated and left on display for the children to match to their toys.
- *Have you ever worn a belt?*
- *Who are you going to make a belt for, Naomi?*
- *Which length of paper strip will you choose? Why?*
- *Will it be a wide or a narrow belt?*
- *How much do you need to cut off?*
- *How tight (long) will the belt need to be?*
- *How well does this belt fit your toy?*

Adaptations

- For an easier activity, provide belts that already match the toys' middles for children to find a suitable match.
- Further challenges include:
  - *Can you make a different belt for the same toy?*
  - *Can you make your belt long enough so that we can do it up* (with glue or a paper clip) *and Teddy can keep it on?*

Does the child ...

- Compare lengths and widths using a range of vocabulary?
- Show an interest in being accurate?
- Recognise similar lengths?

Developments

Moving on

- Provide strips of thin card in different widths for the children to make belts for themselves.

- Children work in pairs, helping to make each other a belt of a chosen width.

What else could you do?

- Use strips of thin material, or ribbons, instead of paper.

- Display a wide range of belts for the children to compare lengths and to try on.

- Provide a selection of containers such as yogurt pots and plastic bottles. Children cut paper strips to fit around the fattest part of the container.

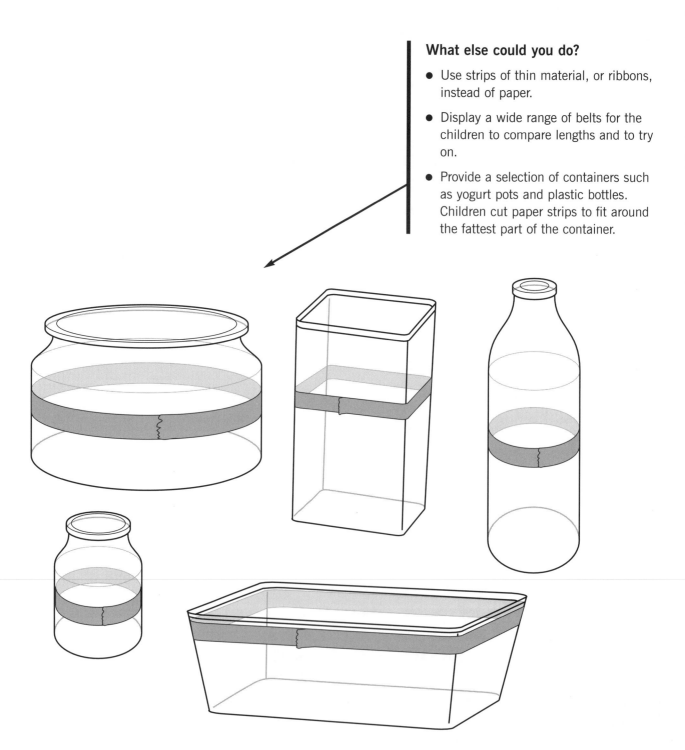

Emptying Out

Description

Children make a simple timer by filling containers with dry sand, then watching how long it takes for them to empty.

Background

- Time is the most difficult measure of all to understand and to measure, as it is both continuous and intangible. This activity is for children to explore and describe the passing of time, comparing short durations. For experiencing a longer period of time, see 'Iced Marbles' (page 92).

- The range of vocabulary describing time is more comprehensive than for any other measure; for example, days of the week, months, ordering events (before, then, next …). 'Emptying out' introduces the vocabulary to describe and compare the passing of time.

- To accurately compare the 'timers', the same amount of sand has to be put into each container. Do not expect all children to be concerned about this, as the main focus of ordering events (before, then, next …) 'Emptying Out' is on introducing the vocabulary to describe the passing of time.

- It will enrich discussions to have a range of commercially produced sand timers (ten seconds, 30 seconds, one minute) for the children to explore. At this stage they will only be able to watch the sand run through, but gradually you may be able to attempt to fit something into the time, for example *I wonder if we can all say our names before this sand timer runs out?*

Working towards these Early Learning Goals

- Use language such as 'greater', 'smaller', 'heavier' or 'lighter' to compare quantities.
- Use developing mathematical ideas and methods to solve practical problems.

Using these Stepping Stones

- Use mathematical language in play.

Who is it suitable for?

- A small group working independently at the sand tray.

Prerequisite knowledge and skills

- Free play with dry sand.
- Ability to watch something happen and talk about it.

Vocabulary

- *time, before, after, today, yesterday, tomorrow, now, soon, early, late, quick, quicker, slow, slower, takes longer, takes less time, What could we try next?*

Emptying Out

We are going to make a sand timer and see how long it lasts

You will need: sand tray, dry sand, scoops, containers such as plant pots with different numbers and sizes of hole in their bases

Main activity

- Pour some sand into a container which has a hole in it (such as a funnel) and encourage the children to say what they see. Model holding one finger, or hand, over the hole, and removing this to stop and start the flow of sand.
- Children explore filling the holed containers and letting them empty out through the holes, stopping and starting the flow of sand.
- *How long did that take until all the sand ran out?*
- *How long will the sand last?*
- *Does this one last a long time?*
- *Is this a quick one? Why?*
- *Tell me about these two bottles.*

Adaptations

- An easier version is to ask the children to play with some sand timers, observing the sand run through.
- Further challenges include:
  - *Find a 'timer' that lasts a long, long time.*
  - *Try to sing all of 'Humpty Dumpty' while your container is emptying.*

Does the child ...

- Talk about what they notice and use some appropriate vocabulary?
- Make any predictions?
- Show a high level of involvement?

Developments

Moving on

- Discuss the children's experiences with the sand.

- Children try emptying some different containers on a given signal, such as *Ready, steady, GO!* Can the children start the flow on the signal?

- Introduce the idea of having a race:

  – Choose two containers and ask for ideas about the one in which the sand will last the longest, and why.

- Have a race where a yogurt pot of sand is put into each container and allowed to flow out on a *Ready, steady, GO!*

- Discuss what happens, encouraging a wide range of vocabulary.

What else could you do?

- Empty bottles of water outside. How long a water line can you make?

- How long does it take to water-paint an outside wall?

- Make your own sand timers by cutting a hole in a coffee filter and placing this in a cup.

Fill It

Area of Maths:
MEASURES:
CAPACITY

Description
Children compare the size of different containers using teddy bear counters.

Background

- 'Fill It' involves these mathematical areas: measuring and comparing container sizes (capacity) plus counting and comparing amounts, and links to work on shape.

- When exploring capacity, there are two experiences to provide: keeping the container the same while changing the measuring unit, and changing the container while keeping the measuring unit constant. 'Fill It' is an example of the latter type. The child can compare sizes of containers as they use the same measuring unit each time. Later, they can learn about different units (rather than different containers) by using one container (for example a small box) and seeing how many of each different unit fills this.

- All measurement is to some degree inaccurate. The degree of inaccuracy that is acceptable varies according to context. Here, two children filling similar containers with the same items will not reach the same conclusions, as their final amount depends on how they fit the counters and when they decide the container is 'full'. These differences are useful for debate and comparison.

Working towards these Early Learning Goals

- Use language such as 'greater', 'smaller', 'heavier' or 'lighter' to compare quantities.
- Use developing mathematical ideas and methods to solve practical problems.
- Use language such as 'circle' or 'bigger' to describe the shape and size of solids and flat shapes.
- Count reliably up to ten every-day objects.
- Say and use number names in familiar contexts.
- Recognise numerals 1 to 9.
- Use language such as 'more' or 'less' to compare two numbers.

Using these Stepping Stones

- Use mathematical language in play.
- Show an interest in shape and space by playing with shapes or making arrangements with objects.
- Use size language such as 'big' and 'little'.
- Show interest by sustained construction activity or by talking about shapes or arrangements.
- Order two items by weight or capacity.
- Count out up to 6 objects from a larger group.

Who is it suitable for?

- Children working independently.

Prerequisite knowledge and skills

- A range of counting experiences.
- Filling and emptying a range of containers with sand and water.

Vocabulary

- *full, half full, empty, holds, container, one, two, three..., count, How many?, more, fewer, altogether*

Fill It

We are going to fill containers with counters and count how many we need

You will need: a range of smallish containers and boxes, such as film canisters, toothpaste boxes, yoghurt pots, and so on, teddy bear counters, or similar counting items all of uniform size
For 'Moving On': sticky notes and pens

Main activity

- Invite the children to each choose a container to fill with teddy bear counters.

- They compare how many counters fit in different sizes and shapes of container.

- *Which pot will you choose to fill up with bears first, Reema?*

- *How many bears do you think will fit inside?*

- *How big is your box?*

- *How many is that so far?*

- *Is your container full?*

- *What did you find out about this container?*

- *Which holds more/fewer bears?*

Adaptations

- An easier version is to keep the range of containers small, as well as keeping their size small, or increase the size of the counting items to fill them.

- Further challenges include:

  - *Put your containers in order of size, from the one that holds most to the one that holds fewest.*

  - *Find a container that holds exactly ten bears.*

Does the child ...

- Tackle the task with confidence?

- Make comparisons and talk about the size of the containers?

- Count the items accurately?

(**Pupil page**)

Fill it

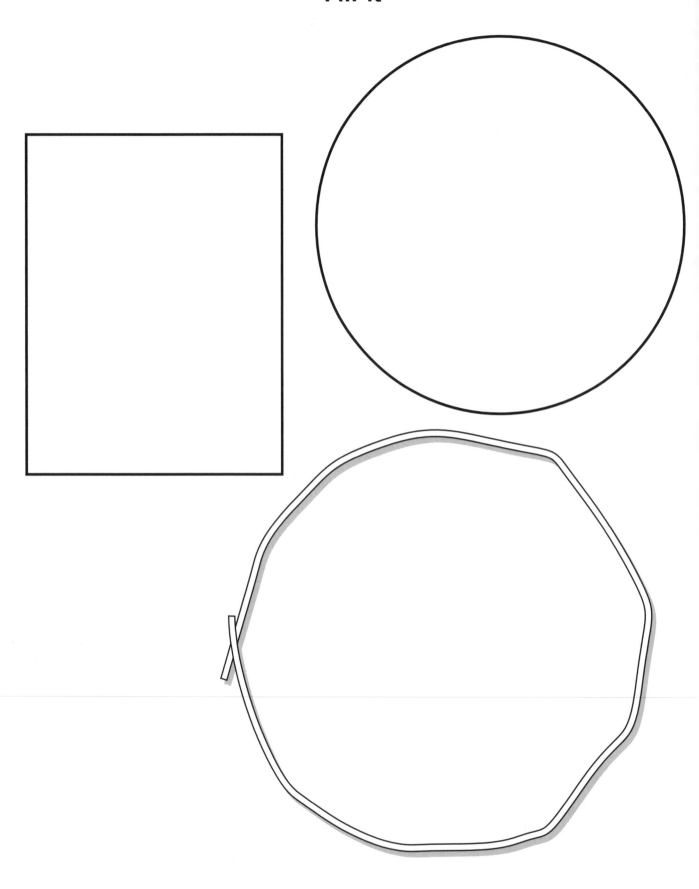

Developments

Moving on

- Look at the table of containers together. Encourage the children to talk about the different sizes of containers, and how they found out they were different.

- Introduce the sticky notes and pens. Model filling a chosen container and writing a sticky note to label how many fit inside.

- If appropriate, change the teddy-bear counters for alternative uniform objects to fill the containers, for example cubes, marbles or beads.

- Children fill containers and write labels for each one they fill, showing the number of items they hold.

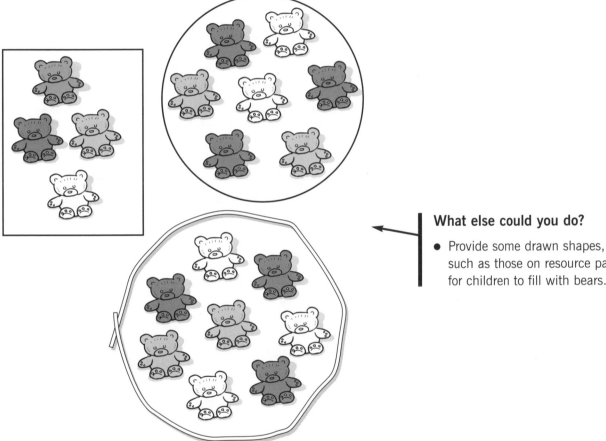

What else could you do?

- Provide some drawn shapes, such as those on resource page A, for children to fill with bears.

- Try filling things with (real) one pence coins and asking: *How much does this hold?*

- Children find how many of different items fit into one container, such as their film canister; provide trays of counting items, such as buttons, beads, mini-dinosaurs, sorting fruits for them to compare.

Iced Marbles

Area of Maths:
MEASURES: TIME

Description

Children watch an ice block defrost, noticing changes over a period of time.

Background

- Time is the most difficult measure of all to understand and to measure, as it is both continuous and intangible.

- The range of vocabulary describing time is more comprehensive than for any other measure; for example: days of the week, months, ordering events in time.

- This activity is for children to explore and describe the passing of time and the vocabulary of duration.

- A litre of frozen water takes about two to three hours to defrost completely in a classroom, so this activity marks a relatively long period of time. To talk about shorter periods of time, see 'Emptying Out' (page 85) and 'Tockers' (page 115).

- Start by displaying the ice block without adult comment and observe those children who display the most interest and curiosity, and those asking questions.

- Iced Marbles is interesting because as the ice melts, the marbles can be 'rolled around' in the ice, eventually dropping out, marking the passing of time with a sound.

Working towards these Early Learning Goals

- Use language such as 'greater', 'smaller', 'heavier' or 'lighter' to compare quantities.

- Use developing mathematical ideas and methods to solve practical problems.

Using these Stepping Stones

- Use mathematical language in play.

Who is it suitable for?

- A whole group as an ongoing activity over a session.

Prerequisite knowledge and skills

- Opportunities to watch and describe what they see happening.

- An interest in things around them.

Vocabulary

- *time, before, after, next, last, now, soon, early, late, quick, quicker, slow, slower, quickly, slowly, takes longer, takes less time, yesterday, today, tomorrow*

Iced Marbles

We are going to see how long it takes for ice to melt

You will need: a frozen litre ice-cream carton of water, containing marbles, a tray

Main activity

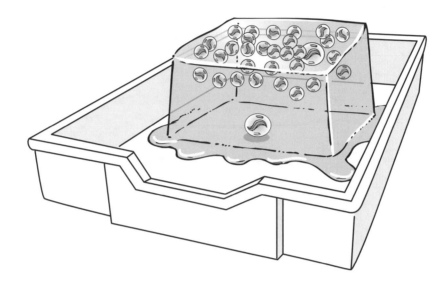

- Prepare a large block of ice containing marbles, by putting marbles into a litre ice-cream carton of water and freezing this overnight.

- At the beginning of a session, turn out the ice-block onto a large tray and leave it where the children can touch it and observe what happens.

- *What can you see, Tom? ... Angela?*

- *What do you notice?*

- *What is happening (now)?*

- *What do you think will happen later ... next?*

- *What was it like before? ... earlier? ... when we came in?*

Adaptations

- For children who need encouragement to talk about what they see, an adult could describe what the child is doing as they touch and explore the block.

- Further challenges include:
  - Encourage them to say when they will return ('after I have played with the bricks'), and to predict what it will be like then ('all these marbles will have fallen out').
  - Ask them to draw what is happening each time they visit the ice block.

Does the child ...

- Show an interest in the activity?

- Talk about what they notice, using some appropriate vocabulary?

- Ask any questions or make any predictions?

Developments

Moving on

- At the end of the session, look at the ice block and ask the children to try to remember what it was like a little earlier, and much earlier.

- Encourage the children to talk about what has happened and how long the block took to melt.

- Ask them to explain how they think you made the ice block of marbles.

- Ask: *What shall we try tomorrow?* Ideas might include melting a larger block, freezing different items inside, putting a similar ice block in a different position.

What else could you do?

- Freeze a number of different objects in a block of ice in layers so that each layer contains something different. Put just enough water into the container to cover the object each time, and then freeze. Remove, add another object and just enough water to cover this, refreeze, and so on.

- Have melting races with ice blocks of different sizes: yogurt pots, margarine tubs, and so on.

- Have an ice cube melting race. Each child has their own ice cube and chooses where to place it in order for it to melt the soonest (before everyone else's); or a slow melting race where each child tries to make their ice cube stay frozen for as long as possible.

Pass It On (2)

Area of Maths:
MEASURES:
CAPACITY (SOME
NUMBER:
COUNTING)

Description

Children learn about capacity in this simple game by counting scoops of sand into and out of, containers.

Background

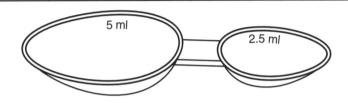

- This game develops 'Pass It On' (page 24). In this version, players count out and pass on scoops of sand. There are no winners and losers, just active participants.

- Playing 'Pass It On' many times, with different resources, will enable children to use their developing skills and knowledge in different contexts. Gradually they will begin to observe and predict, for example 'If I get a three, your pot will overflow!'.

- Playing with wet sand rather than dry sand changes the game: dry sand runs off the spoon, whereas wet sand can be heaped up, making decisions about 'full' different.

- Encourage the children to play independently, by letting **them** organise the turn-taking.

- As the game develops, encourage discussion about how much sand to pass on, which end of the scoop will they use, (if you have a double-ended medicine spoon) and why.

- Over time, varying the containers to hold the sand will draw the older, more experienced children into discussions about what is 'fair' and perhaps a decision on how to 'win' the game.

Working towards these Early Learning Goals

- Use language such as 'greater', 'smaller', 'heavier' or 'lighter' to compare quantities.
- Use developing mathematical ideas and methods to solve practical problems.
- Count reliably up to ten every-day objects.
- Say and use number names in familiar contexts.
- Recognise numerals 1 to 9.

Using these Stepping Stones

- Use size language such as 'big' and 'little'.
- Show interest by sustained construction activity or by talking about shapes or arrangements.
- Order two items by weight or capacity.

Who is it suitable for?

- Group of up to four children working independently.

Prerequisite knowledge and skills

- Opportunities for free play with the scoops and the sand.
- Experience of 'Pass It On' (page 24).
- Ability to count to three.

Vocabulary

- *full, half full, empty, holds, container, one, two, three ..., How many ...?, count*

Pass It On (2)

We are going to scoop sand in and out of the containers and count the scoops while we do it

You will need: a small dish of dry sand for each player, small scoop, such as a double-ended medicine spoon, for each player, one-to-three dot dice for each player

Main activity

- *Come and play 'Pass It On' with the sand.*

- Each child puts some sand in their dish. Each child has their own die but takes it in turns to roll. If they roll a 3 they pass three scoops of sand from their dish to the person sitting next to them.

- Play continues around the table, each child rolling a die and passing that number of scoops of sand from their dish to their neighbour.

- *Have you enough sand to play with?*

- *Who are you passing your sand to, Barry?*

- *Is your scoop (dish) full?*

- *How many scoops will you pass on?*

- *What do you do now?*

- *What happens next?*

- *What's happened to your (Rula's) dish of sand?*

- *What will happen if … ?*

Adaptations

- An easier version is to omit the dice and in turn, each child chooses how many scoops to pass on.

- Further challenges include:

  – *Say how your (or your partner's) dish of sand will change before you pass.*

  – Play with a numeral die.

Does the child …

- Willingly talk about what is happening? ('Look – I've got no sand left!')

- Accurately count the scoops to match the die-roll?

- Show a high level of involvement?

Developments

Moving on

- Ask the children to recall how the game was played.

- Encourage them to remember, and tell us something that happened; perhaps they couldn't pass on any sand. Why was that?

- Provide wet sand and a selection of different sized scoops to play with this time.

- *How will this change your game?*

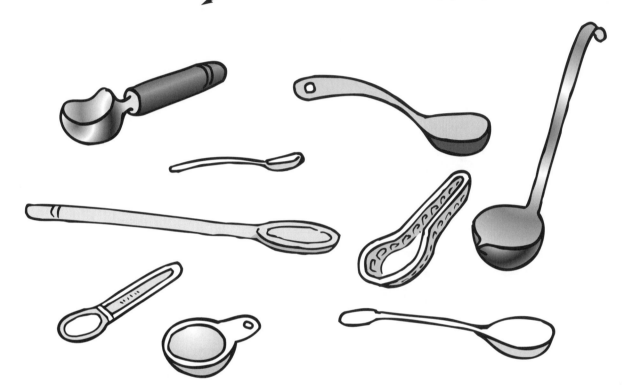

- Support the players in making decisions about how to organise the game: how to share out the sand to start playing, which scoops to use, and so on.

- When the game is well under way, encourage discussions and comparisons about how much sand they are passing on.

What else could you do?

- Each child starts with a container of dry sand in a different colour.

- Try passing on scoops, or yogurt pots of coloured sand.

- Try playing it big, outside, by passing on numbers of seaside buckets of sand or water.

Sandy Socks

Area of Maths:
MEASURES: WEIGHT

Description

Children fill socks with sand to compare weights.

Background

- Children often find it easier to use the descriptive word 'heavy' rather than 'light'. This activity encourages the use of comparative language such as 'heavier **than**' and 'lighter **than**'.

- As the socks fill with sand, they stretch, which is very visual – the children can 'see' the sock getting heavier. Later, filling similar sized 'parcels' with different weights helps the children pay attention to how something feels rather than how it looks. (See 'Heavy Shopping', page 79.)

- Physical experience of making something increasingly heavy are an important precursor to using a weighing instrument such as balances (see 'Stretchy Scales', page 107 and 'Treasure Hunt', page 118).

Working towards these Early Learning Goals

- Use language such as 'greater', 'smaller', 'heavier' or 'lighter' to compare quantities.
- Use developing mathematical ideas and methods to solve practical problems.

Using these Stepping Stones

- Use size language such as 'big' and 'little'.
- Use mathematical language in play.
- Begin to talk about shapes of everyday objects.
- Order two items by weight and capacity.

Who is it suitable for?

- A small group working independently.

Prerequisite knowledge and skills

- Some experience of working collaboratively.
- Sufficient dexterity to hold and fill a sock with sand.

Vocabulary

- *weigh, weighs, heavy, light, heavier than, lighter than, weight*

Sandy Socks

We are going to fill socks with sand and watch what happens

You will need: lots of socks, a large tray of sand, scoops/shovels
For 'Moving on': a number of boxes or paper bags, of a similar size
and shape

Main activity

- Demonstrate how to shovel some sand into some socks, and pass these around encouraging weight discussions and comparisons.
- Children work in pairs to make heavy, heavier, light and lighter socks of sand.
- *What does this sock feel like, Huw?*
- *What happens to the sock when you fill it up with sand?*
- *Hold one sock in each hand – which is lightest?*
- *What can you tell me about the weights of your sandy socks?*
- *Do you think this sock is heavier or lighter than this one?*
- *Why do you think that sock looks (feels) heavier than yours?*
- *What sort of sock are you going to make now?*
- *How far can you carry your sock before you have to put it down?*

Adaptations

- An easier version is where an adult holds the sock for the child to fill and carry.
- Further challenges include:
    - *Make up two socks that feel the same weight.*
    - *Can we put these three (or more) socks in order from heaviest to lightest?*

Does the child ...

- Use comparative words like 'lighter' and 'heavier'?
- Identify correctly which of two socks is heavy and which is light?
- Show a high level of involvement?

Developments

Moving on

- Help the children use a range of vocabulary to discuss and explain their experiences of filling and carrying the sandy socks. *Which was the heaviest sock we could lift? How far could we carry this?*

- Provide a number of boxes or paper bags of a similar size and shape, and sand to fill them.

- Ask the children to make parcels of different weights. Compare the sealed parcels: *Can we find ... two parcels that feel the same? two very different parcels?*

What else could you do?

- Try it big and heavy outside: Shovel sand into bags until they break, or fill tights with wet sand and try and lift them!

- Supply lots of balls of cotton wool to explore 'light' and 'lighter'. Fill bags with different numbers of these. Compare weights.

- Display a range of sealed boxes with lids, each containing different items and some bucket balances for children to compare their weights.

Wrapping It Up

Area of Maths:
MEASURES: AREA

Description

Children cover different sizes of boxes with wrapping paper.

Background

- This activity combines a range of mathematics: measuring and matching sizes, counting, and later, comparing weights; it also links to work on shape. The initial task is to cover a box with paper by 'wallpapering' each face. This is an area task.

- It is worth spending time on the initial discussion of ways of tackling the problem, encouraging the children to come up with their ideas. You may choose to have this discussion again later, pointing out various successful methods.

- Completing this task will take a lot of stamina from the participants, so it is best left to run over a few sessions, allowing the children to return to the problem.

Working towards these Early Learning Goals

- Use language such as 'greater', 'smaller', 'heavier' or 'lighter' to compare quantities.
- Use developing mathematical ideas and methods to solve practical problems.
- Use language such as 'circle' or 'bigger' to describe the shape and size of solids and flat shapes.
- Use every-day words to describe position.

Using these Stepping Stones

- Use mathematical language in play.
- Show interest in shape and space by playing with shapes or making arrangements with objects.
- Show interest by sustained construction activity or by talking about shapes or arrangements.
- Begin to talk about the shapes of every-day objects.
- Adapt shapes or cut material to size.

Who is it suitable for?

- A small group working independently, after initial adult input.

Prerequisite knowledge and skills

- Some dexterity with scissors.
- Opportunities to make things with boxes.

Vocabulary

- *shape, flat, straight, face, side, edge, end, make, build, draw*

Wrapping It Up

We are going to wrap our boxes in paper

You will need: sheets of wrapping paper, glue, a range of different sized boxes
For 'Moving on': collection of objects to go into the boxes

Main activity

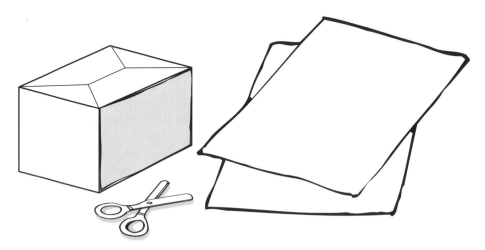

- Children choose a box to cover with wrapping paper.

- Discuss how they might tackle this.

- Encourage the children to draw around each box-face, cut this out and stick it on, until the box is covered with wrapping paper.

- *What is your box like?*

- *What is your idea?*

- *How much paper do you think you will need to cover your box ... the bottom (this face) of your box?*

- *How can you find out how many faces your box has?*

- *Can you tell us how you knew that paper fitted there?*

- *Have you covered all your box?*

Adaptations

- Adult help might be required to draw around the boxes.

- Further challenges include:

  - *Make a lid for your box.*

  - *Cut down each edge of a box to turn it inside-out – cover the other side!*

Does the child ...

- 'Measure' the paper with care to fit the box?

- Talk about the size and shape of boxes/paper using appropriate language?

- Tackle the task with confidence?

Developments

Moving on

● Display the wrapped boxes for discussion, talk to the children about how they solved the problem.

● Use the boxes to do some weighing – children choose objects to place in their boxes. What will they choose and why? How heavy has this made their box?

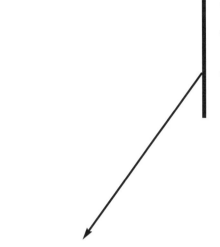

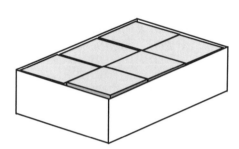

What else could you do?

● Use the boxes for some counting – children choose different objects to place in their boxes. How many will they choose to put in and why? How many (bricks) will their box hold altogether?

● Use the boxes for some reasoning – children hide objects in their boxes. A friend shakes the box to try and guess what may be inside.

● Children cut wrapping paper to wrap up familiar objects for others to guess what they wrapped.

Up to the Line

Area of Maths:
MEASURES:
CAPACITY

Description

Children fill different containers up to a marked line.

Background

- Using smaller containers for water-play allows children to pour and fill more carefully, as it is difficult to hold and/or pour anything as large as a litre bottle steadily.

- Many children pay more attention to the **emptying** container, continuing pouring until this is empty, often until the filled container is overflowing. Using a marked line draws the children's attention to the container that is being **filled**, which is necessary for capacity work.

- It is valuable to have a discussion about how accurately the container has been filled – here we are using the term 'filled' as a verb rather than a descriptive state. *Is this container, a little (lot) too full? ... a little too empty? ... (not full enough?) ... or is it just right?*

- Coloured water helps the children to see how far the water reaches up the container.

- You might find that children work well in pairs, taking turns at pouring and then holding the filling container to say when it is full enough.

Working towards these Early Learning Goals

- Use language such as 'greater', 'smaller', 'heavier' or 'lighter' to compare quantities.
- Use developing mathematical ideas and methods to solve practical problems.

Using these Stepping Stones

- Observe and use positional language.
- Use shapes appropriately for tasks.
- Sometimes show confidence and offer solutions to problems.
- Order two items by weight or capacity.

Who is it suitable for?

- A small group working independently at the water tray.

Prerequisite knowledge and skills

- Free play in the water tray, pouring into and emptying out a range of containers.

Vocabulary

- *full, half full, empty, holds, container, nearly, close to, about the same as, just over, just under, too much, too little, enough, not enough*

Up to the Line

We are going to fill containers up to the line and compare how full they are

You will need: a range of small transparent containers and bottles in different shapes and sizes (funnels may also be necessary), a water tray filled with coloured water, a shelf, plank or table on which to stand filled containers, masking tape, pens (for 'Moving on')

Main activity

- Beforehand, mark a horizontal line on each container. This can be done with a permanent pen, or a strip of masking tape. Vary the position of the lines, with some near the tops of the containers, some halfway, and some near the bottom.

- Explain that the lines are 'fill up to' lines. Demonstrate pouring water into a few different containers. Invite the children to tell you to stop pouring when the water reaches the line.

- Children pour water into a range of containers, just up to the lines, then stand the finished containers on the table.

- *Tell me when to stop pouring.*

- *Is the water up to the line?*

- *Is it a little too full (a little too empty)?*

- *Which container will you choose for pouring? ... to fill first?*

- *How far up is this line?*

- *How much water did you use? ... will you need?*

- *How full (empty) is this container? ... What about this one?*

Adaptations

- An easier version is to omit the lines. One child (or adult) pours the water, another holds an unmarked container and shouts 'stop' when they want the pourer to stop pouring. Can they stop straight away? Change roles.

- Further challenges include:

  - Find three of their completed containers, one that is the fullest, one about half full, and one nearly empty (this is more of a challenge than ordering full containers, as they need to pay attention to only the water-filled part of the container).

  - Draw some of their containers and show how full they are.

Does the child ...

- Take account of the line when pouring water into the containers?

- Talk about what they notice using words like 'full', 'fuller', 'empty', 'emptier'?

- Show a high level of involvement?

Developments

Moving on

- Provide containers, each with a wide, vertical masking tape strip down the side, and some waterproof pens.

- Examine the containers together; encourage the children to discuss how much each will hold when it is full.

- Discuss questions like: *Where is 'half full'? Where is 'nearly empty'? Which of these two bottles will be holding the most water?*

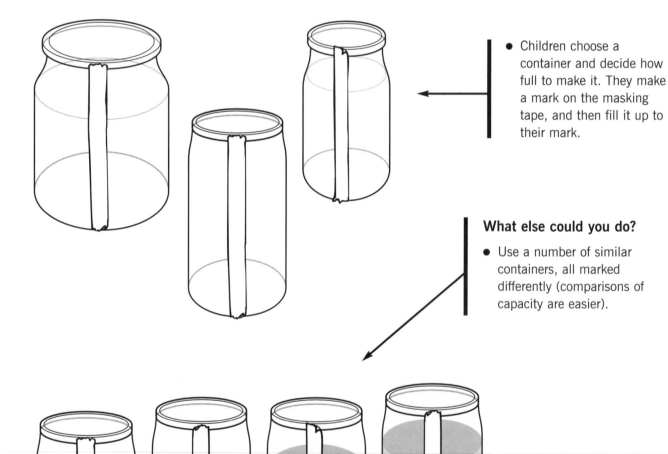

- Children choose a container and decide how full to make it. They make a mark on the masking tape, and then fill it up to their mark.

What else could you do?

- Use a number of similar containers, all marked differently (comparisons of capacity are easier).

- Repeat, using dry sand.

- Try it big, outside, with lines marked on kitchen buckets, and seaside buckets to pour with.

Stretchy Scales

Area of Maths:
MEASURES: WEIGHT

Description

Children use a simple homemade spring balance to compare the weights of different objects.

Background

- Strictly speaking, we are 'weighing' when using a spring balance, and 'measuring mass' when using a rocker-type balance.

- Traditional balance scales can be confusing for some children, as the same mass moves up and down according to what is placed in the other side of the balance. 'Stretchy scales' enriches young children's weighing experiences. The heavier items clearly stretch further down, giving the same feeling as when carrying a bag of shopping.

- All measurement is to some degree inaccurate. The degree of accuracy that is acceptable varies according to the context. Here, the elastic bands do not stretch uniformly and fine comparisons are difficult. The activity is effective for promoting appropriate language and demonstrating larger differences in weight. It helps to have a baseline for the empty scales to return to, although you may not need this until later.

  - These scales also allow us to compare the weights of more than two items, as we can use three or more of them in a row.

Working towards these Early Learning Goals

- Use language such as 'greater', 'smaller', 'heavier' or 'lighter' to compare quantities.
- Use developing mathematical ideas and methods to solve practical problems.

Using these Stepping Stones

- Use size language such as 'big' and 'little'.
- Begin to talk about the shapes of every-day objects.
- Order two items by weight or capacity.

Who is it suitable for?

- A small group with an adult, and later working independently.

Prerequisite knowledge and skills

- Opportunities to watch and describe what they see happening.
- Experience of feeling items of various weights, for example 'Heavy Shopping' (page 79), 'Sandy Socks' (page 98).

Vocabulary

- *weigh, weighs, balances, heavy, light, heavier, lighter, heaviest, lightest, weight, balance, scales*

Stretchy Scales

We are going to use scales to measure how heavy some fruits are

You will need: clean, empty milk cartons, elastic bands, string (to make the scales), a range of fruit, stretchy scales masking-taped to a board or flip chart, felt-tip pens (for the activity)

Main activity

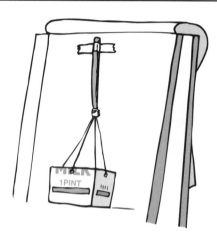

- Beforehand, make several of the scales and tape one to the top of a board or flip chart.

- Invite some children to come and put an item of fruit into the 'pan'. They describe what they see happening, and what they predict will happen with different fruits.

- *What do you think will happen if I put this orange onto the scales?*

- *Why do you think that?*

- *What about* this *orange ... or this Kiwi?*

- *Come and put your finger where you think the scales will stretch down to.*

- *What happened?*

- *Can you choose something heavy that you think will stretch right down to here?*

- *Which is heavier (lighter) ... the orange or the kiwi? How do you know?*

Adaptations

- An easier version is to use fruits with big differences in weight and to start by passing them around to be handled, discussed and compared.

- Further challenges include:
  - *Find the heaviest (lightest) fruit in the bowl.*
  - *Find two different fruits the same weight.*

Does the child ...

- Show some understanding of 'heavy' and 'light' in relation to these scales?
- Use comparative words like 'lighter' and 'heavier'?
- Show a high level of involvement?

Developments

Moving on

- Leave the scales and the items for the children to explore. Expect them to stretch them until they break!

- After every child has had plenty of opportunities to play with the scales, discuss what they have found out about the weight of different fruits.

- Introduce the idea of recording what happens: put in one item and ask a child to make a mark with a pen to show where this stretches to.

- *How can we remember which mark is which?*

- Leave the pens and scales for the children to explore this.

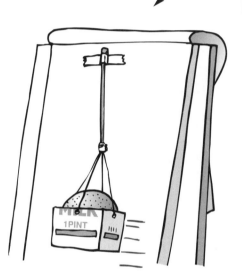

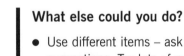

What else could you do?

- Use different items – ask the children for suggestions. Try lots of one item for example, apples of different sizes or different sorts of nuts.

- Hang three or more scales alongside each other, for direct comparisons of more than three objects to be made.

- Weigh potatoes in carrier bags in a similar way.

Strings

Area of Maths:
MEASURES: LENGTH

Description

Children find matching lengths using string as a measuring tool.

Background

- In 'Strings' children compare different length strings with masking tape strips hidden around the room and try to find the tape strip that matches their string-length.

- Matching a length of string to a strip of masking tape, or a drawn line, with a clear beginning and end, draws attention to where to start and finish making the comparison. Commonly, young children place items as shown below to make a comparison.

- Talk about how to line up the string with one end of the tape, and how much is left over at the other end.

- All measurement is to some degree inaccurate. The degree of accuracy that is acceptable varies according to the context. This activity encourages children to decide themselves whether their string is the same length or not. The value of the activity lies in the discussions the children have over the comparisons they make, and each child's decision. Do not be surprised if a child says none are **exactly** the right length! Also, do not expect everyone to agree on the match.

- It is more successful to start by making the lengths of each tape very different.

Working towards these Early Learning Goals

- Use language such as 'greater', 'smaller', 'heavier' or 'lighter' to compare quantities.
- Use developing mathematical ideas and methods to solve practical problems.

Using these Stepping Stones

- Use size language such as 'big' and 'little'.
- Use shapes appropriately for tasks.
- Order two items by length or height.
- Match some shapes by recognising similarities and orientation.
- Order two or three items by length.

Who is it suitable for?

- Small numbers of children working independently.

Prerequisite knowledge and skills

- Recognition of longer and shorter when comparing two similar things of different lengths.
- Ability to watch and describe what they see happening.

Vocabulary

- *length, long, short, tall, longer, shorter, longest, tallest, nearly, close to, about the same as, just over, just under, compare, size, measure*

110

Strings

We are going to find the hidden tape that is the same length as our measuring string

You will need: a different length of string for each child, the longest should be no longer than they can hold tight with outstretched arms, masking tape

---

Main activity

- Beforehand, tape some strips of masking tape of different lengths around the room. Cut lengths of string to match these masking-tape strips.

- Give each child a length of string and explain it is their 'measuring string'. Can they find the hidden masking tape strip that is the same length as their string?

- *Can you see some hidden tapes?*

- *Do you think it looks the same length as your string?*

- *How are you going to measure the tape with your string?*

- *Where will you start measuring? Why?*

- *Do you think it is the same length?*

- *Do you think it is a bit longer (shorter) or just the right length? Why do you think that?*

- *What will you try next?*

- *Look at your string – can you see anything that you think is about the same length?*

Adaptations

- An easier version is to make the differences between the lengths of tape very pronounced.

- Further challenges include:

  – Make the differences between the lengths of tape very slight.

  – What else can they find that is just the same length as their measuring string?

Does the child ...

- Match the end(s) of the string to the end(s) of the masking tape?

- Compare lengths using a range of vocabulary?

- Decide themselves whether the lengths match?

- Become interested in finer degrees of accuracy?

Pupil page

Strings

Pupil page

Long or Short Tails

Developments

Moving on

- Help the children discuss and explain their experiences of measuring with their strings.

- Discuss both their findings and the skills they used when they made comparisons.

- They may wish to repeat the activity with a new string-length that they choose.

What else could you do?

- Longer lengths: Children work in pairs, using a much longer string, to match to long chalked lines outside. Discuss how they will tackle this.

- Omit the masking tape for children to find matching items for their strings.

- Match or cut strings for resource pages A and B.

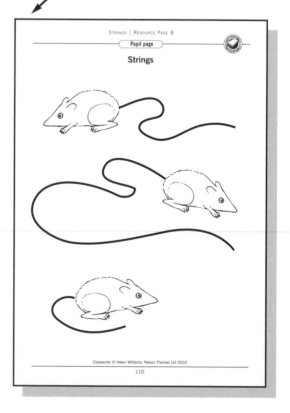

Tockers

Description

Children make a lid rock for different lengths of time.

Background

- Time is the most difficult measure of all to understand and to measure, as it is both continuous and intangible. This activity is for children to explore and describe the passing of time, comparing duration. For experience of a longer period of time, see 'Iced Marbles' (page 92).

- The range of vocabulary describing time is more comprehensive than for any other measure; for example: days of the week, months, for ordering events. In 'Tockers' children practise using vocabulary to compare the passing of time.

- 'Tockers' introduces the idea of 'fitting' something into a period of time, for example: *I wonder if we can finish singing 'Humpty Dumpty' before your tocker stops rocking?*

- A 'tocker' rocks for a varying amount of time, depending upon the position of the Playdough. You can experiment with different amounts and positions of Playdough alongside the children, this will support their decision-making and introduce them to a wider range of vocabulary. The difficulty is in deciding when the 'tocker' has stopped moving.

- Allow the children to participate in making these decisions; paying attention to when something starts and when something finishes is an important part of measuring duration. Drawing a face on the lid helps the children observe the rocking movement.

Working towards these Early Learning Goals

- Use language such as 'greater', 'smaller', 'heavier' or 'lighter' to compare quantities.
- Use developing mathematical ideas and methods to solve practical problems.

Using these Stepping Stones

- Use mathematical language in play.
- Show interest by sustained construction activity or by talking about shapes or arrangements.

Who is it suitable for?

- A small group working with an adult.

Prerequisite knowledge and skills

- Opportunities to play freely with Playdough.
- An interest in things around them.

Vocabulary

- *time, before, after, now, soon, early, late, quick, quicker, slow, slower, quickest, slowest, takes longer, takes less time, What could we try next?, How did you work it out?*

Tockers

We are going to make 'tockers' and see how long they tick-tock for

You will need: circular coffee-jar lids or similar small cylinders, the top of each covered with a circle of paper, Playdough, felt-tip pens

Main activity

- Choose a lid and draw a face on this. Demonstrate pressing a lump of Playdough into the rim of a lid, standing it on its rim and pushing it to make it rock, or 'tock'.

- Encourage the children to say 'tick, tock' as it moves from side to side. Can they say when it stops?

- Children use the lids and Playdough to make their own 'tockers'.

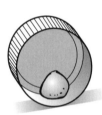 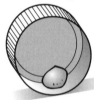  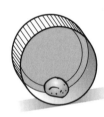

- *How will you make it rock (tick-tock), Lucy?*
- *How much* Playdough *will you use?*
- *How is it working?*
- *Let it keep going until it stops – how long will it last?*
- *Ready, steady, GO!*
- *Where will you try putting the* Playdough *(this time)?*

Adaptations

- An easier version is to have Playdough already in position on some lids for children to experiment with starting and observing the rocking movement.
- Further challenges include:
  - *Make a 'tocker' that lasts a very long (or very short) time.*
  - *Explain what you want to try next.*

Does the child ...

- Show a high level of involvement?
- Talk about what they notice using some appropriate vocabulary?
- Try out some of their own ideas or make any predictions?

(**Developments**)

Moving on

- Discuss the children's experiences making 'tockers'.

- Ask the children to describe the 'tockers' they made.

- Try a 'tocker'. Say: *Ready steady, GO!* and as it starts, the children stand up. As soon as it stops, they all sit. *How long were we standing?*

- Compare some 'tockers' in this way.

- Choose some of the 'tockers' to do some timing. Ask the children for ideas of what to do whilst it is working, for example: *Can we sing a song while it tocks?*

What else could you do?

- Display the 'tockers' alongside cards of familiar illustrated rhymes to read when the 'tocker' is working.

- Explore how long different pendulums swing.

- Display some wind-up toys for the children to compare how long they run.

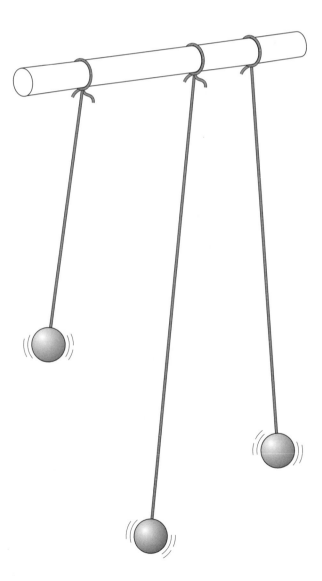

Treasure Hunt

Area of Maths:
MEASURES: WEIGHT

Description

Children play a game in pairs to search for 'treasure' and use a bucket balance to compare weights.

Background

- This activity encourages the use of comparative language such as 'heavier **than**' and 'lighter **than**'. Children often find it easier to use the descriptive word 'heavy' and need encouragement to use 'light'. Physical experiences of feeling and comparing weights, and making something heavier or lighter are an important precursor to using a weighing instrument such as balances (see 'Sandy Socks' page 98 and 'Heavy Shopping' page 79). Strictly speaking, we are 'weighing' when using a spring balance (see 'Stretchy Scales' page 107), and we are measuring mass when using the type of balance used in this activity.

- It is important that children are given plenty of opportunities to play with and talk about how balance scales work. They can be confusing, as the same mass moves up and down according to what is placed on the other side.

- Weighing the treasure in similar bags helps children pay attention to how something feels rather than how it looks.

Working towards these Early Learning Goals

- Use language such as 'greater', 'smaller', 'heavier' or 'lighter' to compare quantities.

- Use developing mathematical ideas and methods to solve practical problems.

- Use everyday words to describe position.

Using these Stepping Stones

- Use size language such as 'big' and 'little'.

- Begin to talk about the shapes of every-day objects.

- Order two items by weight or capacity.

Who is it suitable for?

- Two children working as a pair.

Prerequisite knowledge and skills

- Experience of working in a pair.

- Experience of comparing weight by feel, for example 'Heavy Shopping' (page 79) and 'Sandy Socks' (page 98).

- Free play with the bucket balances.

Vocabulary

- *weigh, weighs, balances, heavy, light, heavier, lighter, heaviest, lightest, weight, balance, scales*

Treasure Hunt

We are going to find hidden treasure and weigh how much we have found

You will need: box of 'treasure' containing necklaces, rings, earrings, bracelets, medals, and so on, bucket balances, two cloth bags, dice with three blank faces and the skull-and-crossbones on three faces made by covering ordinary dice with resource page A, a sand tray

Main activity

- Items of treasure are hidden in the sand tray. Children take it in turns to roll a die.

- If they roll a skull-and-crossbones, they search for a piece of treasure in the sand and put it in their treasure bag.

- When all the treasure has been found, the weight of the bags are compared on the bucket balances.

- *What do you do now?*

- *What happens when you roll a blank?*

- *How much treasure have you found so far?*

- *Do you think that a piece of treasure will make your bag a lot heavier?*

- *Whose treasure bag do you think is the heaviest?*

- *How will you find out?*

- *What can you tell me about the treasure bags now you have weighed them?*

- *Why was Chau's bag so light?*

Adaptations

- An easier version is to omit the dice and to ask the children to 'dig' for treasure to put in their bags to weigh and compare.

- Further challenges include:

  - *Will you have a winner? How will you decide who that will be? What if... the lightest bag wins this time?*

  - Play in a group of three. It is very challenging to find out whose treasure bag is the heaviest/lightest of the three players.

Does the child ...

- Show some understanding of how a set of balances are used?
- Use comparative words like 'lighter' and 'heavier'?
- Play the game co-operatively with a partner and display a high level of involvement?

Resource page

Cover ordinary dice with these covers
to make skull-and-crossbones dice.

Hidden treasure

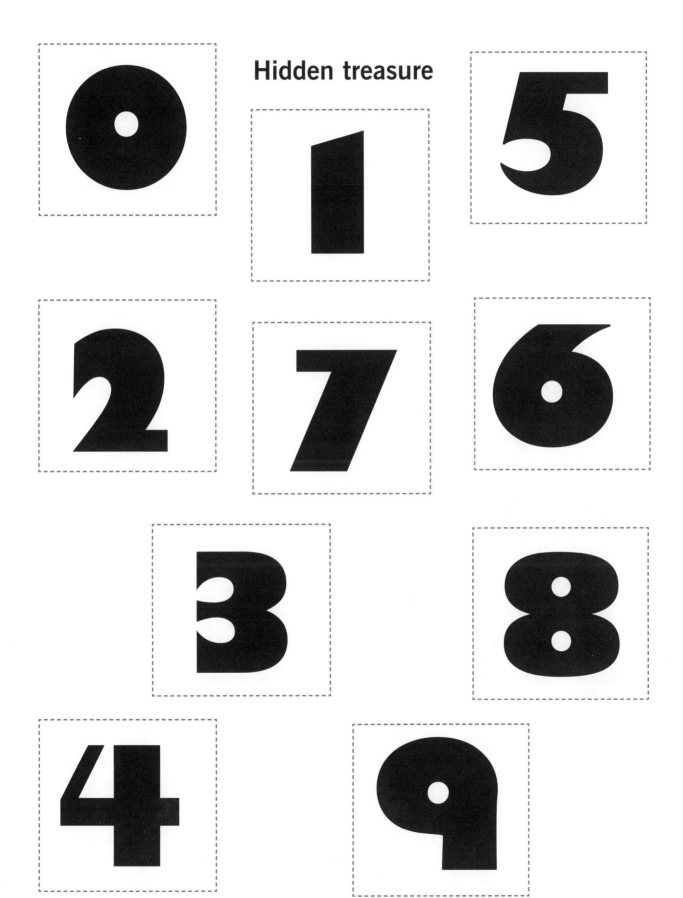

Developments

Moving on

- Encourage the children to talk about their experiences of playing the game. What did they enjoy about it?

- Rather than having one bag each to place their treasure into, they can decide which bucket to add directly to each time allowing more comparisons to be made.

- Encourage children to talk about their decision: *Why did you choose to add the treasure to the lighter (heavier) side?*

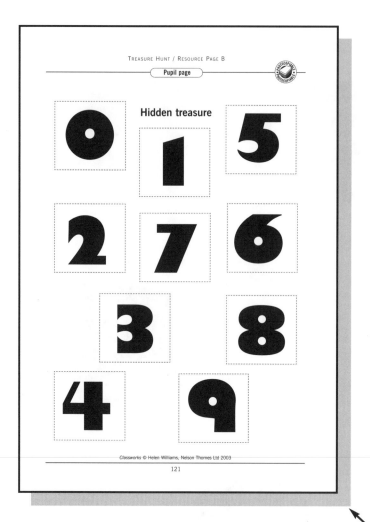

What else could you do?

- Play the game hunting for different things – ask the children for ideas.

- Sunken treasure: Put beads in the water tray and provide strainers to 'catch' them. Each catch is placed in the pan scale, and compared.

- Instead of rolling a die, children pick a numeral and collect that amount of treasure to bag up and weigh.

Trains

Description

Children select rods of different lengths to match a longer length.

Background

- This activity is about fitting items end-to-end to match a given length. Providing rods of differing lengths provides opportunities for making both comparisons and decisions. Encourage the children to talk about the rods they choose and the decisions they make. The overall length of the completed 'trains' of rods can then be compared. Commonly, young children align items as shown below to make a comparison:

- Matching the rods to a drawn line, and then moving on to using 'start' and 'finish' lines, with a clear beginning and end, draws attention to aligning the items correctly, and where to finish making length comparisons.

- Over time you can move onto counting the number of rods it takes to fill a length; this is a precursor to counting and comparing numbers of similar size items (measuring using non-standard, but uniform, units of measurement).

Working towards these Early Learning Goals

- Use language such as 'greater', 'smaller', 'heavier' or 'lighter' to compare quantities.
- Use developing mathematical ideas and methods to solve practical problems.
- Use every-day words to describe position.

Using these Stepping Stones

- Observe and use positional language.
- Begin to talk about the shapes of every-day objects.
- Order two items by length or weight.
- Use language such as 'big' and 'little'.

Who is it suitable for?

- A small group with an adult.

Prerequisite knowledge and skills

- Experience of creating freely with the rods.
- Knowledge of the role of dice in games.
- Ability to count to three.

Vocabulary

- *length, long, short, longer, shorter, nearly, close to, about the same as, just over, just under, match*

Trains

We are going to put rods end-to-end to make a long train

You will need: Cuisenaire rods or number rods, one-to-three dotted or numeral dice for each child, chalk
For 'Moving on': interlocking cubes in single colour trays

Main activity

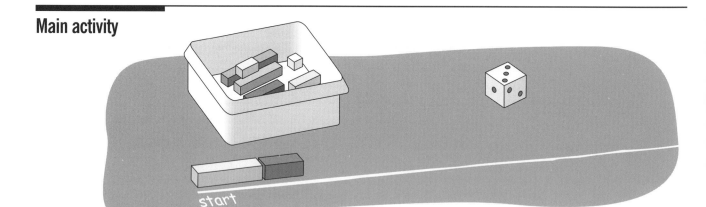

- Start by chalking a long, straight line on the floor to be the length of the 'train'. Explain that the 'train' is made of carriages of different sizes.

- Each player takes it in turn to roll a die and choose that number of 'carriages' from the central collection (tray of Cuisenaire).

- (S)he places these end-to-end to make a continuous line of carriages from one end of the chalked line to the other.

- Players can make their own trains or contribute to a group train.

- *Which carriages (rods) are you going to choose? Why?*

- *How did you reach the finish so quickly?*

- *Are there enough carriages to reach from start to finish?*

- *How long is our train (now)?*

- *Make sure all your carriages touch end-to-end.*

Adaptations

- An easier version is to omit the dice and ask the children to make different length trains from the rods.

- Further challenges include:

  – Try playing so that the player whose train reaches the end of the line first, is the winner.

  – Play so that the winning is the longest train when the rods run out.

Does the child ...

- Consider length when choosing the rods?

- Use a range of length vocabulary appropriately?

- Talk about what (s)he is doing and what is happening?

(**Developments**)

Moving on

- Ask the children to recall how the game was played.

- Play the same game using interlocking cubes.

- Ask the children to choose their cube-colour.

- To play, mark both a start and a finish line on the floor. Children play as before, rolling the dice but this time selecting the correct number of cubes and making a cube-line from the 'start' to the 'finish'.

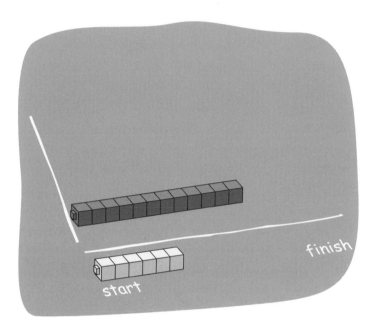

What else could you do?

- Play with Playdough 'worms'.

- Play with items all the same length, such as Learning links; these 'bend' and will allow you to measure around a perimeter.

- Chalk large closed shapes on large sheets of paper, to fill with hand prints (filling an area).

Shadows

Area of Maths:
SHAPE AND SPACE (MAINLY 3-D

Description

Children explore the shapes of shadows of familiar objects.

Background

- Shape-and-space work should include looking at things from different points of view. If children do not learn to do this, they may end up thinking a square is only a square if it is oriented with its edge horizontally, yet in another orientation it becomes a 'diamond'.

- As children build confidence in identifying shadows of objects, we can use more unfamiliar objects and focus on developing their range of descriptive language, rather than simply correctly identifying the object.

Working towards these Early Learning Goals

- Use developing mathematical ideas and methods to solve practical problems.
- Use language such as 'circle' or 'bigger' to describe the shape and size of solids and flat shapes.
- Use every-day words to describe position.

Using these Stepping Stones

- Show an interest in shape and space by playing with shapes or making arrangements with objects.
- Observe and use positional language.
- Begin to talk about the shapes of every-day objects.
- Match some shapes by recognising similarities and orientation.

Who is it suitable for?

- A large group working with an adult at first and later independently.

Prerequisite knowledge and skills

- Familiarity with the chosen objects.
- An interest in things around them.

Vocabulary

- *shape, patterns, circle, triangle, square, rectangle, star, left, right, up, down, bigger, larger, smaller*

Shadows

We are going to look at some shadows and guess what has made them

You will need: an OHP and a set of familiar objects (hidden), a book to 'screen' the objects from the children
For 'Moving on' (see resource page A): a table screened off with material to make it dark underneath, and torches

Main activity

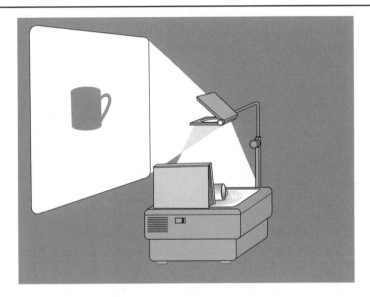

- Secretly choose an object to place on the OHP. Stand a book to 'screen' the object from the children. Encourage them to discuss the shape of the shadow and what they think the object is. Turn the object in order to display some different shadows. Reveal the object and compare it with its shadows.

- *What can you see, Laura?*

- *Is it a bit like something else?*

- *What do you think, Conor?*

- *Here it is again, but another way up.*

- *Could it be a ...?*

- *Why? Why not?*

Adaptations

- An easier version is for the children to choose the initial collection of objects to place on the OHP.

- Further challenges include:

  - Use a structured set of 3-D shapes to make shadows.

  - Children work in pairs to make two different shadows using the same object.

Does the child ...

- Describe both the objects and the shadows using words like 'round, 'straight', 'corner'?

- Take an active part in the activity?

- Recognise familiar objects presented in unfamiliar ways?

Developments

Moving on

- Screen off the legs of a table with material to make it dark underneath.

- Provide a box of objects and some torches for the children to explore the shadows they can make.

- They draw the shape of some of the shadows they have made to talk about later.

What else could you do?

- Ask the children for suggestions for things they would like to place on the OHP.

- Put the objects in a 'feely' bag or under a cloth to identify by feel.

- Provide large sheets of paper and felt-tip pens. Children choose an object, lay it on the paper and draw carefully around the shape it makes. Can a partner find the objects they drew around?

Cylinder Family

Description

Children construct different sized cylinders by rolling thin card.

Background	• It is important that children have opportunities to construct and deconstruct shapes as well as to handle manufactured, regular shapes. 'Cylinder Family' moves between two and three dimensions, transforming a flat sheet of card with straight edges and sharp corners into a curved 3-D shape – magical! This is the opposite of 'Inside Out' (page 132). When modelling the making of the cylinder, repeatedly roll and unroll the sheet of card to demonstrate this transformation. This supports the children's developing ability to visualise and predict.
	• It is harder to use one size of card to make a range of cylinders (see 'Adaptations' on the next page) because although changing the fatness of the cylinder is quite straightforward, changing the height involves turning the card and seeing both the cylinder and the card differently.
	• Using thin card rather than paper gives the cylinders some rigidity, allowing you to make a top and a bottom.
Working towards these Early Learning Goals	• Use developing mathematical ideas and methods to solve practical problems. • Use language such as 'circle' or 'bigger' to describe the shape and size of solids and flat shapes. • Use language such as 'greater', 'smaller', 'heavier' or 'lighter' to compare quantities. • Say and use number names in familiar contexts.
Using these Stepping Stones	• Show an interest in shape and space by playing with shapes or making arrangements with objects. • Use mathematical language in play. • Show interest by sustained construction activity or by talking about shapes or arrangements. • Adapt shapes or cut material to size. • Show curiosity and observation by talking about shapes, how they are the same or why some are different.
Who is it suitable for?	• A small group working independently.
Prerequisite knowledge and skills	• Some experience of working collaboratively. • Some dexterity is required to roll and tape the card.
Vocabulary	• *hollow, solid, flat, curved, make, build, cylinder, bigger, larger, smaller*

Cylinder Family

We are going to make a family of different sized cylinders

You will need: thin card squares and rectangles in different sizes – none too small, tape in dispenser, pens. For 'What else could you do?' (see resource page A): scissors

Main activity

- Demonstrate how to roll a piece of thin card to make a cylinder. Use one piece of tape to hold the roll in place. Stand the cylinder up and draw a face near the top. Make another into a different size.

- Invite the children to make a family of different cylinders in this way.

- *What sort of cylinder is this one, Dan?*

- *Who thinks they can make a really tall (thin, fat, short) cylinder?*

- *Bet you can't make a middle-sized one.*

- *How did you make your really short, fat one, Selma?*

- *What cylinder will you make next?*

- *Tell us about your family of cylinders.*

Adaptations

- An easier version is for an adult to help with the taping.

- Further challenges include:

  – Use only one size and shape of card, for example A4, to make a range of cylinders.

  – *Put a selection of cylinders in order of size – how will you decide how to do this? By height? By fatness?*

Does the child ...

- Show a high level of involvement?

- Talk about what they notice using some appropriate vocabulary?

- Try out some of their own ideas or make any predictions?

Developments

Moving on

- Display the cylinder families for discussion and comparison
  – *are there any the same?*

- Look at a solid cylinder. Roll paper around the outside to
  show the curved face, just like theirs.

- Look at the circular ends of the solid cylinder.

- *I wonder if we can make a top and a bottom for our
  cylinders?*

- Discuss how they might tackle this and encourage the
  children to draw around each end of their cylinder.

What else could you do?

- Identify the cylinders from a
  collection of assorted 3-D shapes
  in a 'feely' bag or box.

- Make cone-shaped 'hats' for the
  cylinders from circles of paper.

- Provide a range of cardboard
  tubes and tins, along with
  wrapping paper for children to use
  to cover the tubes.

Inside Out

Area of Maths:

SHAPE AND SPACE (MAINLY 3-D

Description

Children undo different shaped boxes to explore how some 3-D shapes are constructed.

Background

- It is important that the children construct and deconstruct shapes as well as handle manufactured shapes, meeting irregular as well as regular shapes, and beginning to see how these are constructed.

- 'Inside Out' moves between two and three dimensions, transforming a 3-D shape into a flat sheet of card. This is the opposite of 'Cylinder family' (page 129). Once the box is opened out, it helps to model repeatedly folding up and unfolding the net to demonstrate the movement between two and three dimensions. This supports the children's developing ability to visualise and predict. Children often need encouragement to handle and observe their box carefully before finding where it opens, instead of ripping it open!

- Some boxes are more complicated in their construction than others. Initially, choose the selection carefully, providing boxes that flatten after undoing only one or two edges. Later, you can challenge the children to undo a box with as few cuts as possible.

Working towards these Early Learning Goals

- Use developing mathematical ideas and methods to solve practical problems.
- Use language such as 'circle' or 'bigger' to describe the shape and size of solids and flat shapes.
- Use every-day words to describe position.

Using these Stepping Stones

- Show an interest in shape and space by playing with shapes or making arrangements with objects.
- Observe and use positional language.
- Begin to talk about the shapes of every-day objects.
- Show curiosity and observation by talking about shapes, how they are the same or why some are different.

Who is it suitable for?

- A small group working independently.

Prerequisite knowledge and skills

- Some experience constructing from boxes.
- Some dexterity is required to undo the boxes.

Vocabulary

- *shape, flat, curved, straight, round, hollow, corner, face, side, edge, end*

Inside Out

We are going to undo and flatten out our boxes then see if we can turn them inside out

You will need: a range of boxes in different shapes and different sizes, glue, masking tape

Main activity

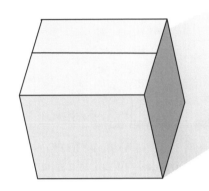
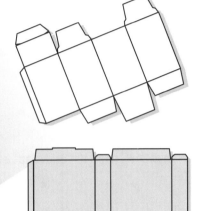
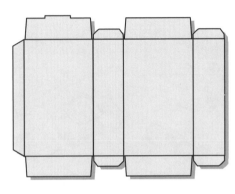

- Children choose a box to undo. Discuss the shape of their box and what they think the box will look like when it has been undone and flattened out. Encourage the children to find the edge(s) where the box is glued and to open this join, until the box flattens. Can they turn the box inside out?

- *Which box will you choose?*

- *What will your box look like when it has been opened up?*

- *Where is the end/side/top/bottom now?*

- *What shapes make up your box?*

- *What box will you try now?*

Adaptations

- An easier version is to choose boxes for children to select which only have one joined edge.

- Further challenges include:
  - Glue or tape the box back together, but inside out. Label the top, bottom and sides before re-gluing the box.
  - Choose more complicated boxes for them to select from, for example, octagonal prism tissue boxes or boxes with several joins.

Does the child ...

- Tackle the task demonstrating both interest and confidence?

- Talk about the shapes using some appropriate 2-D vocabulary?

- Talk about the shapes using some appropriate 3-D vocabulary?

Developments

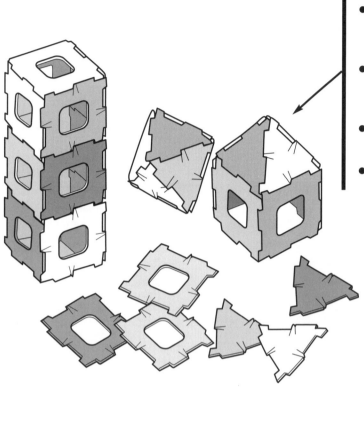

Moving on

- Discuss some different boxes. Demonstrate how these fold up and down from three to two, then two to three dimensions.

- Provide Polydron or a similar shape construction resource and demonstrate how the Polydron joins flat along its edges, and folds up to make a 'box'.

- Invite the children to create their own boxes using Polydron.

- Each child explains to the others how their box is made and what shapes they used to make it.

What else could you do?

- Cut pieces of coloured paper to fit each face of the opened-out box and glue these on. Remake the box with the coloured paper on the outside.

- Provide teddy-bear counters to fit into the boxes: *How many teddy bears can live in your box?*

- Draw plans of boxes you want to make or that you have made.

Castles

Area of Maths:

SHAPE AND SPACE
(MAINLY 3-D) PLUS
SOME POSITION
AND MOVEMENT

 Description

Children work in pairs using a range of 3-D shapes to create a castle for play-people.

Background

- 3-D shape is not only about learning the names of the shapes, but learning about the properties of different shapes, for example *This one's good for rolling/building high with, because ... You can't build on top of this one because ...*

- In 'Castles' children build with a range of shapes, beginning to use a variety of language and vocabulary, both every-day and mathematical, to describe them.

- Being able to talk about what you are doing goes through several stages. At first, children might name what they have completed: 'It's a garage' or 'House'. Later, they might describe what they have done in more detail, and later still describe what they plan to do before actually doing it.

- It is helpful if adults model appropriate language by playing alongside the children and describing either what they are doing or what the child is doing: *I see you are choosing the tall one to make the tower, Selina. Rob – are you using these flat ones to make the path?*

- It is equally important to respond to **how** children make their model as well as to the completed model, for example: *That was tricky making the doorway, wasn't it? Well done for trying hard to make it balance.*

Working towards these Early Learning Goals

- Use developing mathematical ideas and methods to solve practical problems.
- Use language such as 'circle' or 'bigger' to describe the shape and size of solids and flat shapes.
- Use every-day words to describe position.
- Talk about, recognise and recreate simple patterns.
- Say and use number names in familiar contexts.

Using these Stepping Stones

- Show an interest in shape and space by playing with shapes or making arrangements with objects.
- Use shapes appropriately for tasks.
- Show an interest for a length of time on a pre-decided construction or arrangement.
- Use appropriate shapes to make representational models or more elaborate pictures.

Who is it suitable for?

- Children working in pairs independently.

Prerequisite knowledge and skills

- Previous independent free play with 3-D shapes.
- A willingness to create something with building apparatus.

Vocabulary

- *make, build, draw, cube, pyramid, core, sphere, above, below, on, in, in front, behind*

Castles

We are going to make castles for the play-people kings and queens

You will need: for the main activity: collections of 3-D bricks of different shapes, including pyramids, cones, cubes, prisms and a range of cuboids, all in various sizes, play-people queens and kings and pictures of castles mounted near the work area (see resource pages A to C)
For 'Moving on' (see resource page D): a large soft cloth such as a scarf

Main activity

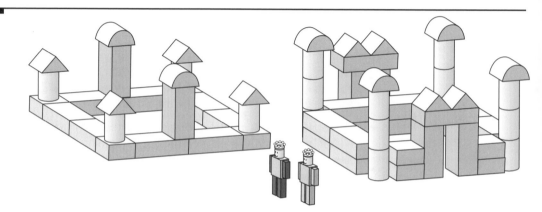

- Look at the pictures of the castles together. Give each pair of children king or queen play-people. They work as a pair to build a castle for them.

- *What do you like about this castle, Zoe?*

- *What shapes will you need to build your castle?*

- *Close your eyes and think about what your castle might look like.*

- *Talk to each other about what you are doing.*

- *Why are you choosing that shape/putting that there?*

- *Talk to me about your castle.*

- *What shapes have you used?*

Adaptations

- Children might find it easier to work in a pair with an adult: *What shall I do, Emma?*

- Further challenges include:

  - *Can you draw your castle?*

  - *How many (cones) have you used?*

Does the child ...

- Maintain attention until the castle is completed?

- Make decisions about what shapes to use?

- Talk about the constructions using some appropriate vocabulary?

Pupil page

Castles

Pupil page

Castles

Pupil page

Castles

Developments

Moving on

● Talk about the shapes the children used in the castle-building activity and what they found they were good for representing.

● Select some of the shapes from the collection used in the castle-building, for example cone, cylinder, cuboid and cube.

● Hide these under the cloth, tucking the cloth tightly around them so that the shapes can be seen.

● Invite the children to look at and feel the shapes through the cloth, describing what they can feel.

● They identify a similar one in the collection, for example 'I think that one's the same because its got a pointy top!'

What else could you do?

● Make up a story about something that happens in your castle.

● Build a large outside castle to play in from large bricks, boxes, or a piece of climbing apparatus covered with a sheet.

● Bury some shapes in the sand tray to identify by feeling them.

Follow the Leader

Area of Maths:

SHAPE AND SPACE (MAINLY 2-D) PLUS SOME POSITION AND MOVEMENT

Description

2-D shapes are used to make a picture which children describe and copy.

Background

- 'Follow the Leader' encourages children to describe each piece and where they place it as they create a design or picture. It is more challenging to describe how something is constructed after the design is completed.

- Providing a sheet of card for each child to work on is necessary so that the pictures are finite, and you can move and compare the completed designs.

- This activity can be repeated with any apparatus; each type alters the demands of the task.

- Using shapes in the same colour makes this a more challenging activity, as children cannot rely on using the names of the colours to identify the shapes.

- It helps if children sit alongside each other when playing in pairs – a shape placed on the right-hand side when sitting opposite someone can be confusing!

Working towards these Early Learning Goals

- Use developing mathematical ideas and methods to solve practical problems.

- Use language such as 'circle' or 'bigger' to describe the shape and size of solids and flat shapes.

- Use every-day words to describe position.

- Talk about, recognise and recreate simple patterns.

Using these Stepping Stones

- Observe and use positional language.

- Begin to talk about the shapes of every-day objects.

- Find objects from position/directional clues.

Who is it suitable for?

- Children working in pairs with adult support.

Prerequisite knowledge and skills

- Free play with the collection of 2-D shapes.

- An ability to make and talk about a picture made with 2-D shapes.

Vocabulary

- *above, below, on, in, in front, behind, beside, next to, left, right, up, down*

Follow the Leader

We are going to 'Follow the Leader' make a picture using shapes

You will need: a set of 2-D shapes, two of each type for each pair and a sheet of A4 card for each child

Main activity

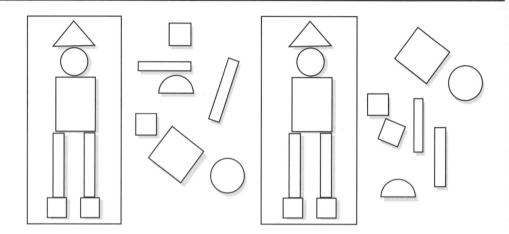

- Model the activity by being a leader for the group to follow. The leader uses some shapes to make a picture on their sheet of card, the others copy what they have done.

- The leader selects shapes one at a time to make their picture. When selecting the shapes, talk about what you choose and where you place it, for example: *I am choosing this circle for his head, and this red triangle for his hat and putting them at the top of my mat.*

- When the pictures are made, compare their differences and similarities.

- *Have you found a red triangle for his hat, Owen?*

- *Are you ready for me to do the next part of my picture?*

- *How are our pictures the same/different?*

- *Can you think of a picture to make for us to follow?*

Adaptations

- An easier version is to provide different shapes in different colours, for example red circles, blue squares and yellow rectangles.

- Further challenges include:

  - Make pictures using different shapes all in the same colour.

  - Add a 'screen', such as a book, between the children, allowing peeps of the picture as it is made.

Does the child …

- Identify some shapes correctly when instructions are given by an adult or a peer?

- Engage in the task using a range of vocabulary?

- Recognise and talk about differences and similarities?

Developments

Moving on

- In pairs, the children sit alongside their partner and take it in turns to lead and to follow.

- When you feel it is appropriate, introduce a screen between the two children, such as a standing book.

- The leader selects shapes to make a picture, like before, describing the shape and where they place it. The follower tries to follow their verbal instructions without looking at the leader's design.

- After a few shapes have been placed, the follower has a 'peep' at the partially completed design, to check that they match.

- Replace the screen and continue.

What else could you do?

- Try 'Follow the Leader' with 3-D shapes and play-people.

- Ask the children to suggest equipment to play 'Follow the Leader' with, for example Cuisenaire rods, Lego, Pattern Blocks, threading beads or shells on a plate.

- Make a complete picture or design, and give children some 'peeps' before describing how to make it, or making it from memory.

Holes

Area of Maths:
SHAPE AND SPACE (MAINLY 2-D) PLUS SOME POSITION AND MOVEMENT

Description

Children explore cutting different shaped holes in folded paper.

Background

- It is important that children construct and deconstruct shapes, as well as handle manufactured shapes, so that they meet irregular as well as regular shapes and learn to classify and talk about all of these.

- 'Holes' explores shapes that are not there! It is quite magical when the folded paper is opened to reveal a hole made without cutting in from the outside edge. Children may need to explore this idea for some time to discourage them from stabbing the scissors into the paper's centre.

- It is quite challenging to make a hole of your choice. Try making a circular or a square hole yourself! You have to concentrate on what it is that makes something circular or rectangular.

- Later, the shapes made can be discussed, compared and classified.

Working towards these Early Learning Goals

- Use developing mathematical ideas and methods to solve practical problems.

- Use language such as 'circle' or 'bigger' to describe the shape and size of solids and flat shapes.

- Talk about, recognise and recreate simple patterns.

- Use language such as 'greater', 'smaller', 'heavier' or 'lighter' to compare quantities.

Using these Stepping Stones

- Show awareness of similarities in shapes in the environment.

- Begin to talk about the shapes of every-day objects.

- Match some shapes by recognising similarities and orientation.

Who is it suitable for?

- A small group working independently.

Prerequisite knowledge and skills

- Ability to use scissors to cut out a specific shape, rather than to snip.

Vocabulary

- *shape, circle, triangle, square, rectangle, star, imagine, describe, talk about, tell me*

Holes

We are going to cut some folded paper and then see what the holes look like when we open out the paper

You will need: lots of scrap paper and scissors

Main activity

- Demonstrate how to fold a piece of paper, pressing along the fold to make it sharp. Children practise this. Cut a hole from the folded side and open up the paper. Talk about what has happened.

- Children explore cutting different shaped holes in folded pieces of paper.

- *How did the hole get in the middle of the paper?*

- *What have you made?*

- *What do you think it looks like? What about you?*

- *What hole do you want to make?*

- *What will you try next?*

- *How did you do that?*

- *What can we call that shape?*

Adaptations

- An easier version is to concentrate on folding and cutting holes out of the correct edge and talking, eventually speculating, about what happens or might happen.

- Further challenges include:

  - *What about making a hole that is a perfect circle/square?*

  - *Cut a big hole and a small hole that are the same shape.*

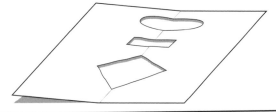

Does the child ...

- Show a high level of involvement?

- Talk about what they notice using some appropriate vocabulary?

- Try out some of their own ideas or make any predictions?

Developments

Moving on

- Display the holey papers near the work table.

- Talk about the different shapes they have made as holes.

- *Which were tricky? Which were easy? Why?*

- Encourage the children to work in pairs, choosing a hole they want to make and helping each other.

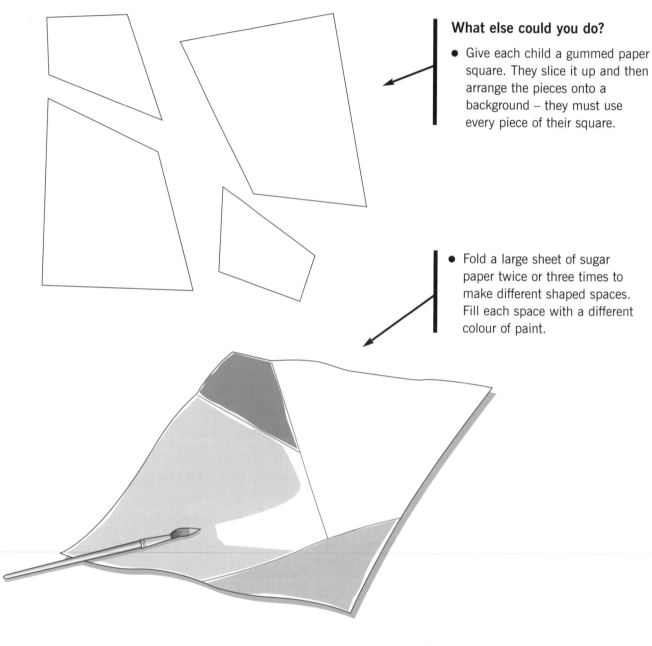

What else could you do?

- Give each child a gummed paper square. They slice it up and then arrange the pieces onto a background – they must use every piece of their square.

- Fold a large sheet of sugar paper twice or three times to make different shaped spaces. Fill each space with a different colour of paint.

- Provide a hole punch and small pieces of paper to fold before punching: *How many holes can you make?*

Circles

Description

Children paint a large circle and then increasingly smaller circles all fitting inside one another.

Background

- It is important that the children construct and deconstruct shapes as well as handle manufactured shapes. This helps them see how a shape is made.

- Nesting items are fascinating for many children and a valuable resource for comparing shapes and ordering sizes.

- A circle is a shape most children recognise as a 'round'. 'Circles' is a 2-D version of the nesting boxes idea.

- As the children become more confident, encourage them to estimate how many circles will fit inside their large circle before they start. The difficult part when you have drawn a number of circles inside one another, is organising the counting. Although many children will not be able to count the circles accurately, it is worth asking for ideas for effective ways of doing so.

Working towards these Early Learning Goals

- Use developing mathematical ideas and methods to solve practical problems.

- Use language such as 'circle' or 'bigger' to describe the shape and size of solids and flat shapes.

- Use every-day words to describe position.

- Talk about, recognise and recreate simple patterns.

- Use language such as 'greater', 'smaller, 'heavier' or 'lighter' to compare quantities.

- Count reliably up to ten every-day objects.

Using these Stepping Stones

- Show awareness of similarities in shapes in the environment.

- Use shapes appropriately for tasks.

- Sustain interest for a length of time on a pre-decided construction or arrangement.

Who is it suitable for?

- A group working independently.

Prerequisite knowledge and skills

- Ability to hold a pen or paint brush and make a closed shape.

Vocabulary

- *draw, circle, bigger, larger, smaller, patterns, inside, outside*

Circles

We are going to try to fit as many circles as possible into our big circle

You will need: paper, and paint in a selection of colours

Main activity

- Ask each child to paint a big circle, then to paint another circle inside it, then another circle inside that, and so on until they cannot fit any more circles inside.

- *How many circles can you fit inside your big circle?*

- *How big will you paint your first circle?*

- *How many do you think you will fit in?*

- *How does using different colours help me count?*

- *What will you try next?*

- *What is the largest number of circles you have painted?*

- *How did you manage to fit eight in, when I have only fitted in four?*

Adaptations

- An easier version is to paint the starting circle for them.
- Further challenges include:
  - Use two (or three) colours and alternate the colours of the circles.
  - Ask the children to draw, say, ten circles inside each other, or to choose a set number to paint.

Does the child ...

- Show a high level of involvement?
- Set her/himself some challenges?
- Talk about what they have done using a range of language?

Developments

Moving on

● Display the paintings of the nesting circles.

● Provide coloured pens and small pieces of paper.

● Invite each child to start with a small circle drawn with a coloured pen.

● Challenge them to fit as many circles inside as they did with the large painted circles.

● Discuss what they find out.

What else could you do?

● Try chalking nesting squares out of doors.

● Display and explore 3-D items that nest together such as Russian dolls, or boxes that fit inside one another.

● Make different sized squares by glueing different lengths of straws onto paper.

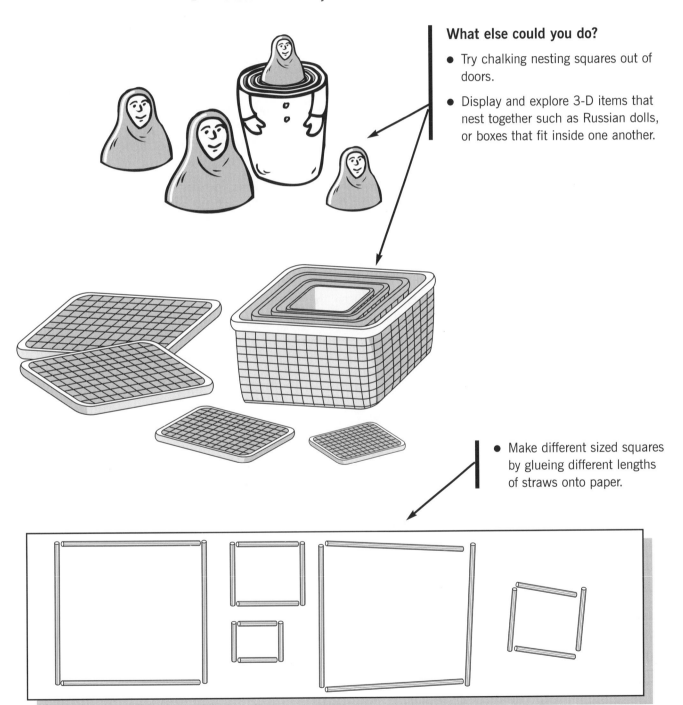

What You Like

Description

Children work with Pattern Blocks to create a design they like.

Background

- 2-D shape is not only about learning the names of the shapes, but also learning about their properties by using them, for example 'This one's good for fitting, because ...'

- In 'What You Like' children use a set of interrelated regular shapes to make a design of their choice, beginning to use a variety of language and vocabulary, both every-day and mathematical, to describe these.

- Being able to talk about what you are doing goes through several stages. At first, children might name what they have completed: 'It's a flower or "pattern"'. Later, they might describe what they have done in more detail, and later still describe what they plan to do before actually doing it.

- It is helpful if adults model appropriate language by playing alongside the children and describing either what they are doing or what the child is doing: *I see you are choosing the diamond shapes to go around the edge, Ahmed.*

- It is important to respond to how the children make their design, as well as the design itself: *You chose the shape to go in the middle very carefully, Sophie.*

- Children do not have the advantage of height to help them see where shapes are in relation to others. Encouraging them to stand and look down on their designs can help them make decisions about where and how to place pieces.

Working towards these Early Learning Goals

- Use developing mathematical ideas and methods to solve practical problems.
- Use language such as 'circle' or 'bigger' to describe the shape and size of solids and flat shapes.
- Use every-day words to describe position.
- Talk about, recognise and recreate simple patterns.

Using these Stepping Stones

- Show an interest in shape and space by playing with shapes or making arrangements with objects.

- Use appropriate shapes to make representational models or more elaborate pictures.

Who is it suitable for?

- Children working independently.

Prerequisite knowledge and skills

- Some dexterity in placing the shapes.

Vocabulary

- *symmetrical, pattern, repeating pattern, match*

What You Like

We are going to choose shapes to make a beautiful design

You will need: Pattern Blocks or similar sets of mosaic shapes and a camera

Main activity

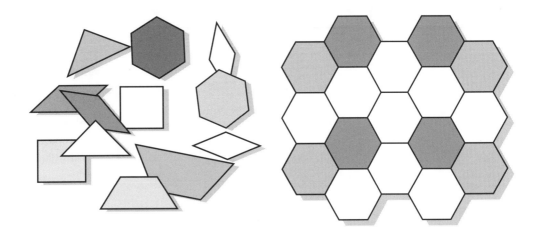

- Ask the children to help each other make something beautiful with the shapes.

- Take photographs of the designs both while being constructed and when completed. Ask each child to talk about what they did and the shapes they used. Add these captions to the display afterwards.

- *Just play with them for a while, Sam, and you will have an idea.*

- *What shapes did you/will you use?*

- *Where did you place that triangle?*

- *Stand up and look down at your design.*

- *What can you see in David's pattern?*

- *What do you like about this one, Tamsin?*

- *Talk to each other about what you are doing.*

- *Why are you choosing that shape/putting that there?*

Adaptations

- An easier version is for children to work with an adult: *What shall I do, Tom?*
- Further challenges include:
  - *Can you draw your design?*
  - *What will you make now?*

Does the child ...

- Show a high level of involvement?
- Make decisions about what shapes to use?
- Talk about the designs using some appropriate vocabulary?

Developments

Moving on

- Display the photographs and the captions for discussion.

- Ask the children to identify individual shapes making up the completed designs: *Where can you see this square, Anna?*

- Provide children with A4 card sheets.

- Children make a design on the card, and cover it with another sheet of card.

- They give their partner peeps, then the partner tries to say what they see during each peep.

- Allow lots of peeps!

What else could you do?

- Try to remake a photographed design.

- Make a Pattern Block road by drawing two parallel lines for the road to fill with blocks.

Feel It

Area of Maths:
SHAPE AND SPACE
(MAINLY 2-D)

Description

Children use touch to find matching lids for a range of containers.

Background

- Shape work is not only about learning the names of the shapes, but learning about their properties, for example 'This one is good for rolling because ...' and 'You can't stand that one on there because ...'.

- In 'Feel It' the children use touch to identify shapes, beginning to use a variety of shape, space and measures language, both every-day and mathematical, to describe these.

- This task is more challenging if the shapes of the containers are very similar.

Working towards these Early Learning Goals

- Use developing mathematical ideas and methods to solve practical problems.

- Use language such as 'circle' or 'bigger' to describe the shape and size of solids and flat shapes.

- Use language such as 'greater', 'smaller', 'heavier' or 'lighter' to compare quantities.

Using these Stepping Stones

- Show an interest in shape and space by playing with shapes or making arrangements with objects.

- Use shapes appropriately for tasks.

- Show curiosity and observation by talking about shapes, how they are the same or why some are different.

Who is it suitable for?

- Children playing in pairs.

Prerequisite knowledge and skills

- Experience of fitting things inside other things.

Vocabulary

- *flat, curved, straight, round, corner, face, side, edge, end*

Feel It

We are going to find the lids for the containers by feeling their shape in the bag

You will need: cloth bags, small containers of different shapes, all with lids
For 'Moving On' (see resource page A): paint, in shallow trays

Main activity

- Look at a collection of containers and their lids with the children. Invite them to identify a lid that fits a chosen container before trying it.
- Ask for help putting a selection of the lids into the bag.
- Children take it in turns to choose a container and feel inside the bag to find its lid.
- *What shape are you feeling for?*
- *What can you feel?*
- *Why do you think that is the right lid?*
- *Is this the right lid? How do you know?*
- *Can you explain how to play?*

Adaptations

- An easier version is to have the collection of lids and containers visible.
- Further challenges include:
  - Have in the collection some lids that don't fit.
  - *Can you make this into a game?*

Does the child ...

- Engage in the task, making some decisions?
- Explain their decisions and ideas?
- Use a range of shape, space and measures vocabulary?

Developments

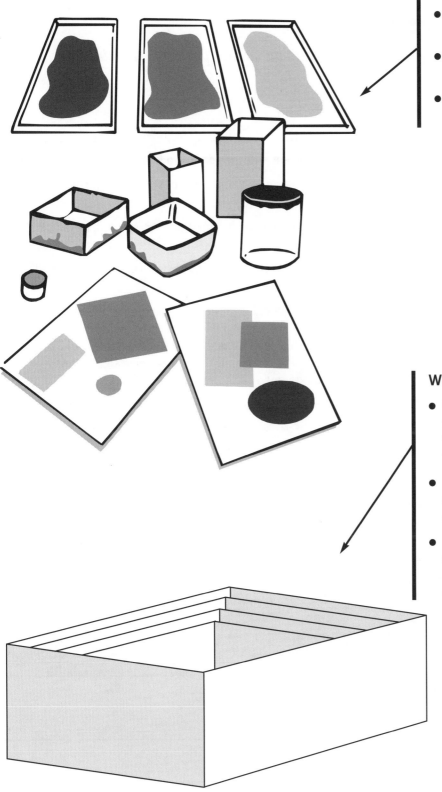

Moving on

- Use the containers for printing:
  - Provide paint in shallow trays.

- Children choose a container and print with its faces.

- Children identify which containers made which prints.

What else could you do?

- Hide a selection of coins in the bag for children to find ones that are all the same shape. Include one, two, twenty and fifty pence coins.

- Provide containers in a range of sizes. Ask the children to find containers to fit inside one another.

- Provide containers, card, pens, scissors, tape in dispensers, and invite the children to make their own lids for the containers.

Picnic

Area of Maths:
SHAPE AND SPACE (MAINLY POSITION AND MOVEMENT)

Description

Children describe positions by taking part in a picnic.

Background

- There are two aspects of movement and position to work on:
  - Developing the vocabulary to describe the position of something in space, for example 'behind' and 'on top'.
  - Developing the vocabulary to describe movement through space, for example 'turn around' and 'go backwards'.
- 'Picnic' uses a role play context to develop children's positional language (see also 'Missing' page 169).
- Children do not have the advantage of height to help them see where objects are in relation to other objects. Encouraging children to stand and look down on their friends seated around a table cloth helps them see where someone is in relation to others. Looking down on something, alongside using small-world toys, helps develop this idea of a 'map'.
- Many children of this age will draw the plan of the picnic with the children in a row along one side of the cloth.

Working towards these Early Learning Goals

- Use developing mathematical ideas and methods to solve practical problems.
- Use every-day words to describe position.
- Say and use number names in familiar contexts.

Using these Stepping Stones

- Observe and use positional language.
- Show interest by sustained construction activity or by talking about shapes or arrangements.
- Find objects from positional/directional clues.

Who is it suitable for?

- A small group with an adult, later independently.

Prerequisite knowledge and skills

- Opportunities for role play in the home corner.
- Free play with small-world toys.

Vocabulary

- *over, under, above, below, on, in, outside, inside, in front, behind, beside, next to, left, right, up, down*

Picnic

We are going to describe where we sit for a picnic.

You will need: a table cloth with a clear design, a basket of picnic ware, biscuits, fruit or similar picnic-food to share, paper and pens
For 'Moving on' (see resource page A): small rectangles of cloth and small-world toys

Main activity

- Lay the cloth on the floor and invite the children to sit around the edge for a 'picnic'. Allow them to choose where to sit and how to arrange themselves around the picnic cloth. Encourage talk about the cloth design.

- Each child stands up and 'looks down'. Discuss where everyone is positioned. Invite the children to share out the picnic-ware and the picnic-food.

- *Where have you chosen to sit, Jemma?*

- *What (who) can you see?*

- *Have you ever been on a picnic?*

- *Who is next to/near/opposite/beside Jon (in between Anne and Kamil)?*

- *Describe what you can see when you stand up and look down at us all.*

- *Let's change places. Where will you go Sanjeet?*

Adaptations

- An easier version is to concentrate on using one phrase, for example 'next to' and on sharing out the plates and food.

- Further challenges include:
  - *Draw the picnic cloth with everybody in position.*
  - Invite a child to tell the others where to sit, without pointing.

Does the child ...

- Describe where children are sitting, using words like 'next to' and 'beside' or 'between'?

- Take an active part in the activity?

- Respond to positional and descriptive vocabulary used by an adult?

Developments

Moving on

- Provide small rectangles of cloth and some small-world toys.

- Children work in pairs to take the play-people for a picnic.

- When they have set up, they come and tell you how they have chosen to arrange the play-people.

What else could you do?

- Change the shape and size of the cloth and the number of picnickers.

- Lay out a cloth with a 'number of the day' to say how many people can picnic today.

- Provide felt squares in different colours and sizes for place mats. Children can play with these if they can accurately request the square(s) they want, for example 'Please can I have the middle-sized, dark blue one?'.

Footsteps

Area of Maths:
SHAPE AND SPACE (MAINLY MOVEMENT)

Description

Children make trails to follow, and describe where they have been.

Background

- There are *two* aspects of movement and position to work on:
  - Developing the vocabulary to describe the position of something in space, for example 'behind' and 'on top'.
  - Developing the vocabulary to describe movement through space, for example 'turn around' and 'straight ahead'.
- 'Footsteps' focuses on developing children's language to describe movement and direction, which is often more difficult to describe than position. Of course, these two aspects are linked and using positional vocabulary is an important part of this activity.
- You might choose to model the vocabulary and the activity by laying a trail of string for a child to follow, encouraging the spectators to join in as you describe where the string leads.

Working towards these Early Learning Goals

- Use developing mathematical ideas and methods to solve practical problems.
- Use every-day words to describe position.
- Talk about, recognise and recreate simple patterns.
- Use language such as 'greater', 'smaller', 'heavier' or 'lighter' to compare quantities.

Using these Stepping Stones

- Observe and use positional language.
- Begin to talk about the shapes of every-day objects.
- Describe a simple journey.

Who is it suitable for?

- Children working in pairs.

Prerequisite knowledge and skills

- The ability to talk about what they have done and where they have been.

Vocabulary

- *corner, direction, left, right, up, down, forwards, backwards, sideways, across, to, from, towards, away from, turn*

Footsteps

We are going to leave footprint trails to help our partner find the hidden toy

You will need: one toy to hide and two sets of cut-out footprints (photocopied and enlarged resource page A) per pair

Main activity

- Children work as a pair. One child secretly hides a toy and lays a trail of footsteps from an agreed starting point to the hidden toy. As they lay the trail, encourage the child to describe where they are going: 'Around the cupboard ... straight ahead ... under the chair ... and out of the door.'

- When invited, the seeker follows the footsteps to find the toy, in turn describing where they are going as they move along the trail.

- *Where have you hidden teddy?*

- *How will you get to teddy?*

- *Where will you go next?*

- *Have you been under / over / around?*

- *Have you turned yet?*

- *How can you make it a longer/shorter trail?*

- *Which way are these footsteps leading?*

- *Describe where you are going.*

Adaptations

- An easier version is to focus on positional vocabulary such as 'under', 'over', 'through' and 'between'.

- Further challenges include:

  – Encourage them to describe the route they will take before starting.

  – *Draw a map of your route.*

Does the child ...

- Take an active part in the activity?

- Describe a route using words like 'straight ahead', 'around', 'over', 'under'?

- Respond to movement vocabulary used by an adult?

Footsteps

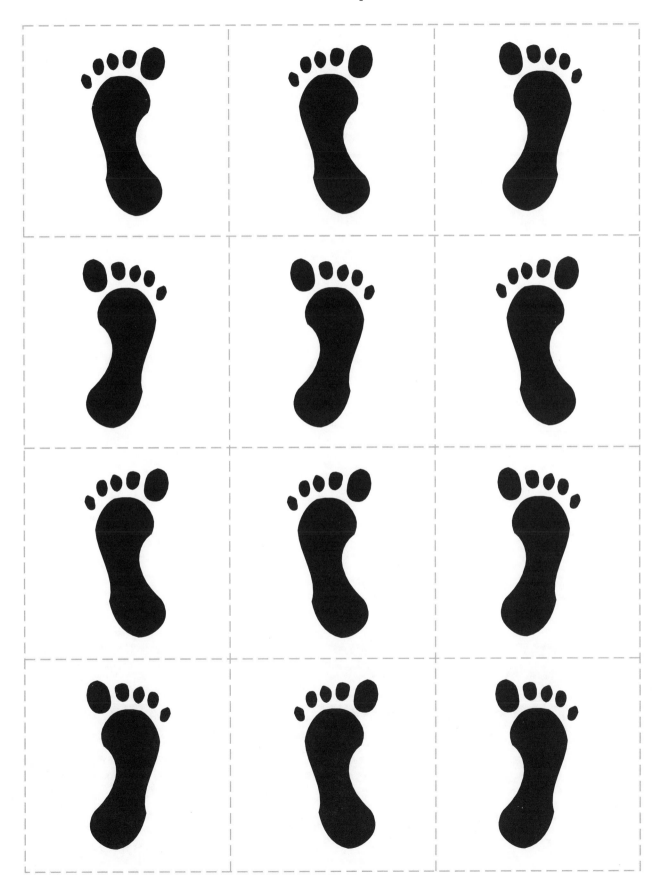

Classworks © Helen Williams, Nelson Thornes Ltd 2003

Developments

Moving on

- Develop the activity outside.
- Position some landmarks.
- Provide chalk for the children to mark routes for the bikes to take.

What else could you do?

- Make wet footprints to follow outside.

- Make journeys for small world toys.
- Provide and create road networks for toy cars.

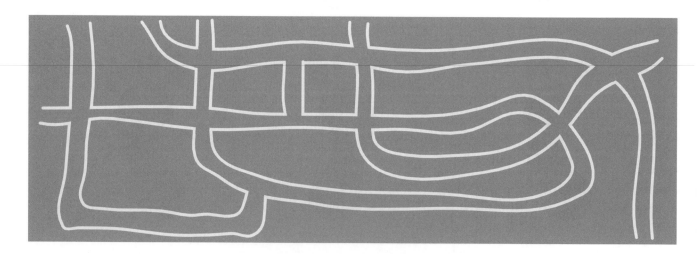

Classworks © Helen Williams, Nelson Thornes Ltd 2003

Mirrors

Area of Maths:
SHAPE AND SPACE (MAINLY PATTERN)

Description
Children use a pair of hinged mirrors to make reflected patterns.

Background

- One of the most enjoyable aspects of mathematics for many children is pattern-making. It is creative and is not seen as being 'right' or 'wrong'. An ability to recognise pattern in all its aspects is a critical part of thinking mathematically. Children will benefit from being given opportunities over time to explore pattern-making with sight, hearing and touch.

- In 'Mirrors' children create visual, reflective patterns. It is important to respond to how they make their design as well as the design itself, for example: *I see you are carefully choosing all the pink ones to put around the outside, Maria. You chose the one to go in the middle very carefully, Omar.*

- If the children are unfamiliar with mirrors, they need opportunities to use them in role play to see themselves dressed up, to pull faces and so on. Providing small-world toys to place in front of the mirrors can engage some children, as it is easier to see how these objects multiply and reflect.

Working towards these Early Learning Goals

- Use developing mathematical ideas and methods to solve practical problems.
- Use every-day words to describe position.
- Talk about, recognise and re-create simple patterns.
- Use language such as 'greater', 'smaller', 'heavier' or 'lighter' to compare quantities.
- Say and use number names in familiar contexts.

Using these Stepping Stones

- Observe and use positional language.
- Show interest by sustained construction activity or by talking about shapes or arrangements.
- Show awareness of symmetry.

Who is it suitable for?

- A small group working independently.

Prerequisite knowledge and skills

- Some familiarity with mirrors.

Vocabulary

- *symmetrical, pattern, repeating pattern, match*

Mirrors

We are going to make some patterns and see how they look when they are reflected in mirrors

You will need: Coloured translucent counters or similar, pairs of safety mirrors joined along one edge with tape to make a 'hinge' (one pair per child) and A4 white card

Main activity

 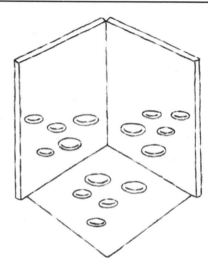

- Stand each pair of hinged mirrors around a sheet of card. Each child sits in front of the hinged mirrors and uses the translucent counters to make patterns on the card.

- *Where will you place that blue counter? What has happened?*

- *What are you going to try now?*

- *Describe your pattern to me so I can make one.*

- *What happens when you place one counter in the corner where the mirrors meet?*

- *How many (green ones) can you see (now)?*

- *What happens when you move the mirrors slowly together/apart?*

Adaptations

- An easier version is to provide small-world toys to place in front of the mirrors.
- Further challenges include:
  - *Make a pattern with only six counters.*
  - Provide paper and coloured pens for them to draw their patterns.

Does the child ...

- Show a high level of involvement?
- Talk about what they notice using some appropriate vocabulary?
- Create some patterns of their own?

Developments

Moving on

- Talk about the different patterns they have made.

- Have they all noticed that the mirrors increase the number of counters you can see?

- Put one object in between the mirrors and move the mirrors first in towards the counters/other objects, then out and away from them.

- Each child has three counters to investigate what happens.

- *What if you put four mirrors together to make a sort of box?*

What else could you do?

- Make pattern-block designs in front of the mirrors.

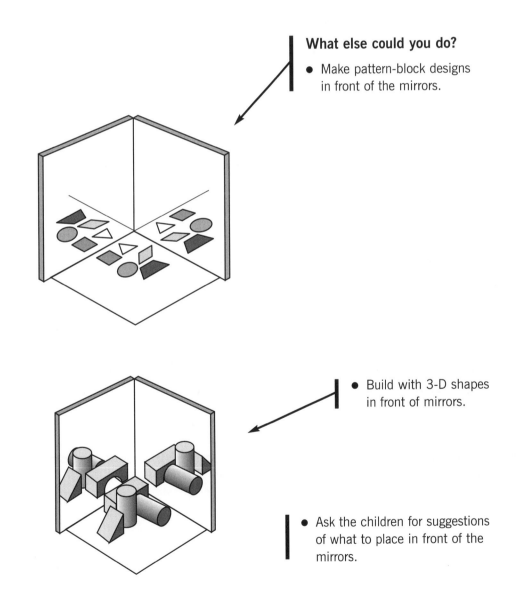

- Build with 3-D shapes in front of mirrors.

- Ask the children for suggestions of what to place in front of the mirrors.

Join In

Area of Maths:

SHAPE AND SPACE (MAINLY PATTERN)

Description

Children make and speak repeating patterns as a 'choral' activity.

Background

- An ability to recognise pattern in all its aspects is a critical part of thinking mathematically. In order to do this we need to have created patterns in many different contexts. Children will benefit from being given opportunities over time to explore pattern-making using a range of senses including sight, hearing and touch.

- 'Join in' is a collective activity where pupils explore repeating patterns vocally and aurally.

- It is easier to recognise a pattern when items are repeated singly, for example 'apple, orange, pear, apple, orange, pear...' than to recognise and create a pattern repeating a restricted number of items a varying number of times, for example 'Apple, apple, orange, apple, apple, orange, apple, apple...'.

- Laying the items out for the children to see while they hear the pattern might be a useful introduction to this activity.

Working towards these Early Learning Goals

- Use developing mathematical ideas and methods to solve practical problems.
- Talk about, recognise and re-create simple patterns.
- Say and use number names in familiar contexts.

Using these Stepping Stones

- Show an interest in shape and space by playing with shapes or making arrangements with objects.
- Show interest by sustained construction activity or by talking about shapes or arrangements.
- Sustain interest for a length or time of a pre-decided construction or arrangement.

Who is it suitable for?

- A large group sitting in a ring.

Prerequisite knowledge and skills

- Willingness to participate in a larger group.

Vocabulary

- *shape, pattern, repeating pattern, match*

Join In

We are going to sing a pattern using the names of different fruit

You will need: a selection of fruit – at least one of each item

Main activity

- Lay a selection of different pieces of fruit a row.
- Start by pointing to a piece of fruit and saying its name all together on your signal: *Apple, apple, apple …*
- Try pointing to and saying two pieces of fruit alternately: *Apple, orange, apple, orange, apple …*
- Try alternating three items: *Apple, orange, banana, apple, orange, banana, apple …*
- You could also say:
  - *Listen to/watch the pattern and join in when you can.*
  - *What comes next?*
  - *How do you know?*
  - *Can you describe that pattern?*
  - *Can you see it* **and** *say it?*

Adaptations

- An easier version is to keep to two or three items repeated singly or make the line of fruit as you say it. (You need multiple items of each fruit for this.)
- Further challenges include:
  - Make a deliberate mistake for them to spot and describe.
  - Ask a child to be the leader and create a pattern for us to join in with.

Does the child …

- Take an active part in the activity as part of a large group?
- Follow the pattern?
- Attempt to describe the pattern?

Developments

Moving on

- A leader touches, and says the name of, a chosen fruit (mango) and then another fruit (banana).

- The next child touches, and says the name of, the last fruit (banana) and touches and says the name of a new fruit (orange).

- Each child takes it in turn to touch the last fruit and choose a new one to add to the pattern.

- Try remembering the two previous fruits.

What else could you do?

- Provide rubber fruit and long strips of card for making patterns.

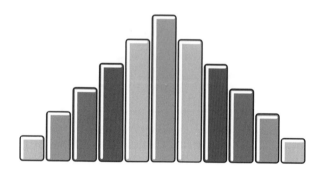

- Tape-record some spoken patterns with resources like sorting toys, for children to follow.

- Explore patterns that 'grow' such as staircases made with Cuisenaire rods.

Missing

Area of Maths:

**SHAPE AND SPACE
(MAINLY MOVEMENT
AND POSITION)**

Description

Children examine a small collection of toys and say what is missing and from where.

Background

- There are two aspects of movement and position to work on:

  – Developing the vocabulary to describe the position of something in space, for example 'behind' and 'on top'.

  – Developing the vocabulary to describe movement through space, for example 'turn around' and 'go backwards'.

- 'Missing' develops a well-known party game to promote children's positional language (see also 'Picnic' page 156).

- You could start by playing 'Odd one out' – providing a collection of similar objects, for example all cows and one sheep, and asking children to explain which is the odd one out, and why.

- Changing the arrangement of the items on the tray each time you play makes this a more challenging task, in terms of both memory and descriptive language. Placing the objects in a line makes it easier to describe the position of the missing object.

- For children to play independently, the adult must step back from organising the game.

Working towards these Early Learning Goals

- Use developing mathematical ideas and methods to solve practical problems.
- Use every-day words to describe position.
- Count reliably up to ten every-day objects.

Using these Stepping Stones

- Observe and use positional language.
- Show interest by sustained construction activity or by talking about shapes or arrangements.
- Show curiosity and observation by talking about shapes, how they are the same or why some are different.

Who is it suitable for?

- A small group working with an adult.

Prerequisite knowledge and skills

- The ability to name all the objects on the tray.

Vocabulary

- *pattern, match, describe, talk about, explain, remember, same, different, missing*

Missing

We are going to see if we can work out what is missing from a tray of toys

You will need: a tray of five familiar objects, for example a pen, teddy, brick, ball and dinosaur, plus a cloth to cover the tray

Main activity

- The children take a good look at the tray of objects. Cover the tray and secretly remove one object. Uncover the tray. Invite the children to say what is missing and where the missing item was.

- Children can take it in turns to be in charge of the tray.

- *What do you think, Justin? ... and you, Alice?*

- *Are you sure?*

- *How do you know?*

- *Sit on your hands. Can you tell me where the ... was?*

- *How are you working it out?*

Adaptations

- An easier version is to ask the children to name each object every time before covering the tray, or to keep the arrangement of the items consistent.

- Further challenges include:

  – Provide more objects which are all very similar to each other, for example five writing implements or five different counting resources.

  – Change the arrangement of the objects on the tray each time.

Does the child ...

- Correctly identify the missing objects(s)?

- Explain position using appropriate vocabulary?

- Respond to positional and descriptive vocabulary used by an adult?

Developments

Moving on

- Explain that you have hidden some toys (for example mini dinosaurs or teddy-bear counters) around the room. Discuss likely hiding places.

- Send children off to search.

- When they find one, they bring it back to you and tell you where they found it, for example 'On top of the brick box' or 'Under the cushion'.

What else could you do?

- Have a 'tray of the day'. Invite a child to choose the objects for the tray.

- Draw all the objects on the tray in exactly the right positions.

- Hide toys outside to find.

Dough Patterns

Area of Maths:

**SHAPE AND SPACE
(MAINLY PATTERN
AND 2-D)**

Description

Children press circular objects into dough and describe the patterns.

Background

- Children benefit from being provided with a range of opportunities to create shapes and patterns. In 'Dough Patterns' the children press circular shapes with different patterns and textures into dough and they are encouraged to use a variety of language and vocabulary, both every-day and mathematical, to describe them.

Working towards these Early Learning Goals

- Use developing mathematical ideas and methods to solve practical problems.
- Use language such as 'circle' or 'bigger' to describe the shape and size of solids and flat shapes.
- Use every-day words to describe position.
- Talk about, recognise and recreate simple patterns.
- Use language such as 'greater', 'smaller', 'heavier' or 'lighter' to compare quantities.

Using these Stepping Stones

- Use size language such as 'big' and 'little'.
- Begin to talk about the shapes of every-day objects.
- Begin to use the mathematical names for 'solid' 3-D shapes and 'flat' 2-D shapes, and mathematical terms to describe shapes.

Who is it suitable for?

- Children working independently.

Prerequisite knowledge and skills

- Free play with dough.

Vocabulary

- *flat, curved, straight, round, face, side, edge, end, circle, pattern*

Dough Patterns

We are going to make some different patterns in the dough

You will need: dough, a selection of wheels from construction sets and other circular objects like cotton reels and lids

Main activity

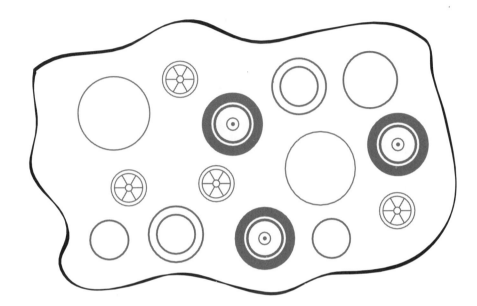

- Roll out the dough thickly. Children choose objects to press into the dough and talk about the patterns and shapes they make.
- *What shape does that make?*
- *Tell me about the pattern that wheel leaves.*
- *What made that pattern in your dough?*
- *What will you try now?*
- *Can you count the prints you have made?*

Adaptations

- An easier version is to provide a range of familiar objects to press into the dough to be identified.
- Further challenges include:
  - Children work in pairs, identifying which objects made which of their partner's prints.
  - *Find some new objects which are smaller/larger than those you pressed.*

Does the child ...

- Engage in the task using a range of shape, space and measures vocabulary?
- Recognise and talk about differences and similarities?
- Use the objects to make a pattern?

Developments

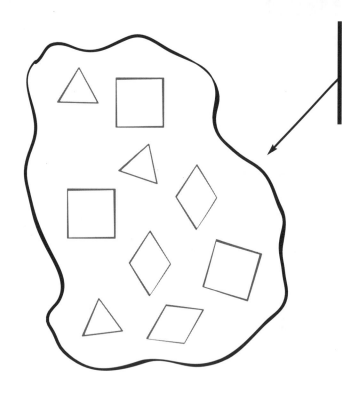

Moving on

- Invite the children to talk about what they found out.

- Ask: *What shall we try next? Lots of square things? Triangular things?*

- Try some of the children's ideas.

What else could you do?

- Use the same objects to make prints.

- Try making rubbings of different textures.

- Children make shoe prints by standing in a tray of paint and printing the pattern on the sole of their shoe. Find shoe-patterns that are similar and different.